THROUGH THE EYES OF A PRISONER

THROUGH THE EYES

BOOK 3

KENNETH A. WINTER

JOIN MY READERS' GROUP FOR UPDATES AND FUTURE RELEASES

Please join my Readers' Group so i can send you a free book, as well as updates and information about future releases, etc.

See the back of the book for details on how to sign up.

* * *

Through the Eyes of a Prisoner

Book 3 of the *Through the Eyes* series

Published by:

Kenneth A. Winter

WildernessLessons, LLC

Richmond, Virginia

United States of America

kenwinter.org

wildernesslessons.com

Edited by Sheryl Martin Hash

Cover design by Dennis Waterman

Cover photo of Paul by Lightstock

Cover background photo of Mamertine Prison by Todd Bolen / BiblePlaces.com

Paul's Missionary Journey Map by Broadman & Holman Publishers © 2003 – Reprinted and used by permission.

ISBN 978-1-7349345-8-8 (soft cover)

ISBN 978-1-7349345-9-5 (e-book)

ISBN 978-1-7367155-0-5 (large print)

ISBN 978-1-7367155-2-9 (hard cover)

Library of Congress Control Number: 2021913417

DEDICATION

To each one who has said farewell to family and friends to travel to another land to share the Good News with those who have not yet heard.

* * *

But how can they call on Him to save them unless they believe in Him? And how can they believe in Him if they have never heard about Him? And how can they hear about Him unless someone tells them? And how will anyone go and tell them without being sent? That is why the Scriptures say, "How beautiful are the feet of messengers who bring good news!"

Romans 10:14-15

* * *

CONTENTS

FROM THE AUTHOR

A word of explanation for those of you who are new to my writing.

* * *

You will notice that whenever i use the pronoun "I" referring to myself, i have chosen to use a lowercase "i." This only applies to me personally (in the Preface and Epilogue). i do not impose my personal conviction on any of the characters in this book. It is not a typographical error. i know this is contrary to proper English grammar and accepted editorial style guides. i drive editors (and "spell check") crazy by doing this. But years ago, the Lord convicted me – personally – that in all things i must decrease and He must increase.

And as a way of continuing personal reminder, from that day forward, i have chosen to use a lowercase "i" whenever referring to myself. Because of the same conviction, i use a capital letter for any pronoun referring to God throughout the entire book. The style guide for the New Living Translation (NLT) does not share that conviction. However, you will see that i have intentionally made that slight revision and capitalized any pronoun referring to God in my quotations of Scripture from the NLT. If i have violated any style guides as a result, please accept my apology, but i must honor this conviction.

Lastly, regarding this matter – this is a personal conviction – and i share it only so you will understand why i have chosen to deviate from normal editorial practice. i am in no way suggesting or endeavoring to have anyone else subscribe to my conviction. Thanks for your understanding.

* * *

PREFACE

Therefore I, a prisoner for serving the Lord, beg you to lead a life worthy of your calling, for you have been called by God.[1]

* * *

This work is a fictional novel set during true events as recorded in the New Testament. At its core, it is a story of the mission of God. A fictional storyline has been created to weave certain parts of the narrative together. The narrator and main character of the story – the apostle Paul – wrote thirteen of the twenty-seven books that comprise the New Testament. Those letters to the churches (which we call "books"), combined with the Book of Acts (as written by Luke), give us a detailed account of one-third of Paul's life story. There are, however, periods of his life that are not specifically recorded in Scripture. Those periods include:

- the first twenty-nine years of his life, prior to his becoming a persecutor of the church in Jerusalem
- the three years he spent in Arabia immediately following his conversion on the Damascus Road
- the seven years he spent in Cilicia and Syria before Barnabas brought him to Antioch

- the final six years of his life that followed his release from Roman house arrest at the end of the Book of Acts.

God ordained before the beginning of time for Paul to become the apostle of the Lord Jesus Christ to the Gentiles. He was given the responsibility of being the "point of the spear" in carrying the Good News to the non-Jewish peoples of the world. Many of us are familiar with the account of how Jesus called him to that responsibility on the road to Damascus. But God had been at work in Paul's life long before that day. God had been preparing Paul – without his knowledge – from birth for that assignment. The same is true of you and me. God was at work in our lives long before we first realized it. He is always at work preparing us for what He is preparing for us. And He has ordered all our steps according to His timing.

Our Lord, in His infinite wisdom, chose not to include those "missing" years of Paul's life in Scripture, just as He chose to not include most of the details about the first thirty years of Jesus's earthly life following His miraculous advent. God did not deem those details to be crucial to His Gospel message.

So, why am i attempting to fill in the gaps with a fictional narrative? Allow me to first say very clearly that it is not my attempt to add to Scripture. This is a *fictional* narrative. Though Paul's epistles give us some hints about those "gaps," i have taken the liberty of creating events and people to underscore the fact that God was using those years to prepare Paul for what was ahead. Paul's journey with Jesus in the mission of God was not a multitude of singular events, it was a lifelong marathon. I have written this narrative to underscore the fact that the same is true for us.

God arranged for Paul to be an accomplished student of the Scriptures under the teaching of one of the greatest rabbis of the day – Gamaliel. God would use Paul to establish much of the doctrine of the early church through his epistles to the churches, and all of what he said and wrote needed to be solidly placed on the foundations laid out in what we now know to be the "Old Testament." Paul needed to be well-founded in those Scriptures.

Jesus spent three years teaching and equipping the other apostles to prepare them to engage in the mission He would give them just before He ascended into heaven. Following a similar pattern, He directed Paul to go to the Arabian wilderness (east of Judea) for a three-year period to also be taught and equipped for his mission to carry the Good News to the Gentiles.[(2)] And Paul tells us Jesus was his teacher.[(3)] He doesn't explain how Jesus taught him. The stories in this novel related to that period of time are intended to underscore the fact that Jesus was personally preparing him. In the Gospels, we see how Jesus taught His disciples then sent them out to apply His teaching. There is no reason to believe He didn't follow a similar pattern with Paul.

Also, it is doubtful Paul would have been content to remain on a mountaintop for those three years. That is not the pattern Jesus followed, nor is it the way we see Paul reacting. Don't forget, he began to preach about Jesus in the synagogues in Damascus immediately after his sight was restored.[(4)] Paul would not have been one to just sit around.

After Paul met with Peter and James (the half brother of Jesus) in Jerusalem, he traveled home to Tarsus. The city became his base of ministry as he began to carry the Gospel to the Gentiles. He evangelized in the regions of Syria and Cilicia,[(5)] planting churches as he went.[(6)] Also, it is very likely that some of the trials he writes about in 2 Corinthians 11:24-36 occurred during this period, including at least a half dozen beatings at the hands of the Jews, as well as the Romans. He apparently was shipwrecked twice during that period. Those seven years were anything but a cakewalk! Through those years, the Gospel was being preached and the kingdom advanced among the Gentiles long before he and Barnabas were reunited in Tarsus.[(7)]

It's also important for us to remember that Paul did not retire for his final six years of life on this earth. He was faithful to continue in the work that God had called him to do, right up until he took his last breath by order of Emperor Nero. i include the narrative of events as a reminder to each of us to finish the race and endure to the end.[(8)]

As the story unfolds, you'll be reintroduced to many from the pages of Scripture, and you will be introduced to several fictional characters that have been added to advance the storyline. You will notice i have even carried forward some of the fictional characters introduced in my previous books, *Through the Eyes of a Shepherd* and *The One Who Stood Before Us*. My purpose is to remind us that many of the people whose lives were touched by Jesus throughout His ministry were still on the scene when we first encounter Paul in the Book of Acts and during the years that followed.

You'll also come across fictional twists and turns that are an attempt to fill in the blanks where Scripture is silent regarding day-to-day events. i have included a character listing as an appendix at the back of the book where i describe the factual and fictional framework for each character. My prayer is that nothing in the story detracts from scriptural truth, but rather by being true to the biblical story, i tell it in a way that creates an interesting and enjoyable reading experience for you.

Throughout the novel, numerous instances of dialogue are direct quotes from Scripture. Whenever i am quoting Scripture, you will find it has been italicized. The Scripture references are included in the back of the book. Those remaining instances of dialogue and teaching not italicized are a part of the fictional novel to help advance the storyline. i have tried to use Scripture as the basis in forming that dialogue wherever possible, with the intent that i do not do anything that detracts from the overall message of God's Word or the character of the people we find in Scripture, including Paul.

i have also included two other resources in the back of the book. One is a timeline of the chapters; in the hopes it will assist you in understanding the chronology of events in Paul's life before and after the crucifixion and resurrection of Jesus. The second is a map which reflects the paths of Paul's three missionary journeys as recorded in the Book of Acts.

Lastly, as you will see in the first chapter, i have chosen Aristarchus to be the scribe for this novel. As we know, Paul's eyesight prevented him from actually writing most of the content in his letters. He would dictate his message to one of the men who was traveling with him. i also wanted the story to include Paul's death, which meant that some of the story would be written posthumously. Paul described Aristarchus as his "fellow prisoner"[(9)] and "fellow worker,"[(10)] and he was frequently his traveling companion, so I thought he was a logical choice.

My prayer is this novel enables you to gain greater understanding of the apostle Paul and recognize that he in no small way was used by God to equip each of us in our walk with Christ. And the purpose of that equipping was not for us to simply grow in our knowledge; rather, we have been equipped by the Word of God (a good portion penned by Paul) and empowered by the Spirit of God for the sake of Christ's mission and the glory of His name. Each of us who names the name of Jesus has been called to join Him in His mission. i pray you are challenged through Paul's faithfulness to the mission of God and inspired to run the race that God has set before *you*. Parts of this story may be fiction – but the Good News and the mission are not! i pray Jesus finds us faithful in following Him in His mission.

And as the apostle Paul said many times, may the grace of the Lord Jesus Christ be with you!

* * *

1

He went to the synagogue service, and for three Sabbaths in a row he used the Scriptures to reason with the people.[1]

* * *

My name is Aristarchus. The story you are about to read is not my story, though my life has been changed for all of eternity because of it. I am but a humble scribe chosen by our Lord Jesus Christ to hold the pen and write the words spoken by my fellow prisoner. Though the writing is mine, the words are his.

We are in the city of Rome, which I am told is the grandest city in the world. It is the political, economic, and cultural center of the Roman Empire and it is said that all roads lead here. But I have not witnessed the grandeur of the city..Even though this is my second journey to Rome, my experience and my view of the city have been very limited. Most recently, my view has been confined to the walls of a prison cell.

This prison was originally built to be a cistern several hundred years ago. Years later when the spring dried up, it was turned into a dungeon and given the name "the Tullianum" in honor of the third Roman king, Tullus Hostillus. Prisoners are lowered into the dungeon through a small opening in the ceiling. The walls and floor are a mixture of stone and dirt, knit together by the mold and mildew of our dark and damp surroundings. The only light is from a few rays of sunshine that make their way through the opening in the ceiling at certain times of the day.

Unlike other prison cells my fellow prisoner and I have shared, this prison is used for only one purpose – to confine those who are awaiting execution for being convicted enemies of the empire. That is the fate awaiting my fellow prisoner. I have not been convicted of anything. I share this cell with him by my own choice. I have been granted special permission to stay with him and be his companion until that fateful day arrives.

He and I have known one another for eighteen years, and I have been his travel companion for much of that time. I will never forget the day we met!

My friend Jason had invited me to his home to hear the teachings of a Jewish tentmaker. He had only recently arrived in our city of Thessalonica, but he had already created quite a stir. As was the practice of the Jews, he had gone to the local synagogue on their Sabbath. He used their Scriptures to remind them of their prophetic writings about a coming Messiah. He was obviously a learned man, with an excellent command of the Jewish Scriptures and an effective ability to communicate their teachings. Jason confided to me that he believed these teachings were true.

The tentmaker went on to share about a Man named Jesus who had lived and died … and risen from the grave. He declared to them, *"This Jesus I'm telling you about is the Messiah."*[(2)] Some of the Jews who listened were persuaded and believed, while others took offense and rejected his teachings.

For those of us non-Jews gathered in Jason's home, the Spirit of God confirmed in our hearts that Paul was speaking truth. For three weeks we continued to gather as our new teacher taught us from the Scriptures. Our number grew with each passing day.

But apparently, some of the Jews were offended that he taught us from the Jewish text. They stirred up a mob in the marketplace and led the riotous group to Jason's home. They sought to do the tentmaker harm – but he was not there at the time. This made the mob even angrier, so they dragged Jason, me, and several others out into the crowd.

They marched us before the city council and shouted, "A foreigner has entered into our midst who has *caused trouble all over the world! And now he is here disturbing our city, too. Jason has welcomed him into his home. They are all guilty of treason against Caesar, for they profess allegiance to another king, named Jesus."*(3)

The crowd was demanding we be punished. Every eye turned to the politarch for his pronouncement. He was the governor of our city council, and the people considered him wise and fair. They knew he would not tolerate civil disobedience of any kind. They also knew he could not turn a blind eye to any rebellion against our Roman leaders.

He stared at me for a long time as he motioned for the crowd to quiet down. Then he turned to look at Jason and the others who stood accused with us. But he turned his gaze back on me when he began to speak. I knew that penetrating look. I had experienced it many times. It was a look that demanded truth. It was a gaze that could not be endured if there was even a hint of guilt.

But I returned his steadfast gaze. We had committed no crime against our city or against Rome! There was nothing for which we needed to admit guilt – unless the acceptance of truth had now become a convictable offense in our city!

. . .

"You have heard the accusation that you are guilty of treason against Caesar and profess allegiance to another king – one by the name of Jesus. How do you respond to that charge, Aristarchus?" the politarch demanded.

The politarch knew my name – in fact, he knew most everything about me. He and I share the same name, the same blood. Though all of us called him politarch, I alone called him father.

"We are guilty of no such thing," I proclaimed. "Jesus is not a political king. He is the Son of the Living God. He came to this world as a baby and lived a sinless life. He taught all who would listen how we are to love the one true God with all of our hearts, soul, and mind. We are to love Him and love one another. He did not come to establish a political kingdom; He came that we might know and experience the kingdom of heaven. He came to teach us how to live an abundant life.

"Then twenty years ago, almost to this very day, another mob falsely accused Him before the prefect of Judea. Jesus died on a cross that day – but He didn't die because He was a criminal, He died to pay the price for our sin. But the grave couldn't hold Him, and three days later He rose from the dead. Jesus is alive. He is Savior – not only of the Jews, but of us all. Through Him and by Him, we receive forgiveness for our sins. No political king can do that for us. We haven't pledged our lives to Him as our political king, we have surrendered our lives to Him as our Lord God.

"We do not follow Him in secret. There is nothing treasonous about what we have done! And I pray that everyone within the sound of my voice will also surrender their lives to Him today. I pray that – most of all – for you, father!"

The crowd gasped when they heard this. They had gotten so caught up in their false accusations and emotions, they hadn't even recognized that I was the politarch's son. All eyes now turned to my father.

. . .

"Citizens of Thessalonica," he began, "those standing before you are your neighbors and are respected members of this community. They have answered this charge, and I find nothing treasonous about their declaration. We receive their word as their surety – and I add my word as surety for my son. They are released. This crowd will disband and return to your homes. No further rioting will be tolerated. And I, for one, will ponder all that has been said."

Later that night, we regathered in Jason's home. Several more joined us ... including my father.

That is how I met my friend Paul and his traveling companion, Silas. The Lord God had providentially kept them away from Jason's home that day. God had known I needed to be the one to stand before my father and respond to the charge of the mob. I needed to bear witness, and my father needed to hear me. It was just one of many ways that God sovereignly orchestrated Paul's steps – always for His divine purpose.

So, please turn your attention to my friend Paul as he tells his story – a story of mercy and grace. A story of faithful obedience to the mission Jesus has placed before him ... and in many ways, before us all.

* * *

2

I am a Jew, born in Tarsus, a city in Cilicia, and I was brought up and educated here in Jerusalem under Gamaliel. As his student, I was carefully trained in our Jewish laws and customs. I became very zealous to honor God in everything I did.[(1)]

* * *

My name is Paul, but some of you also know me as Saul. I was given both names at the time of my birth. Saul is my Hebrew name in light of my Jewish heritage. Paul is my Roman name since I am a recognized citizen of the Roman province of Cilicia.

During my early years, I used my Hebrew name exclusively since I mainly interacted with other Jews. In more recent years, I have primarily been in contact with Gentiles scattered throughout the Roman Empire, so I now use my Roman name. Some have said I changed my name to Paul because of other changes in my life – but that is incorrect. I was given both names at birth, which is another example of how Jehovah God prepares us for that which He is preparing for us in the days ahead – often long before we realize it. But enough about my name!

. . .

I am the son of Jacob – the son of Abiel, who was the son of Sheba, the son of Gera, the son of Zeror, the son of Becorath, the son of Aphiah. We are all descendants of the tribe of Benjamin, the youngest son of Jacob, whom God renamed Israel. All of those I have mentioned were Pharisees, beginning with Aphiah.

He was a man of valor who fought bravely alongside of Judas Maccabaeus in the revolt of our people that led to our independence from the Seleucid Empire. After our people attained freedom, two sects arose in the leadership and governance of our people.

One was the Pharisees, who advocated for strict adherence to the Mosaic laws, as well as the oral rabbinical teachings and traditions. The Pharisees pride themselves on rightly knowing and interpreting the law. The other primary sect is the Sadducees. They dispute the oral teachings and deny the resurrection of the dead. My ancestor Aphiah was one of the first Pharisees, and each of his descendants followed in that tradition.

My great-grandfather Sheba became a tentmaker and made the decision to move his family from Jerusalem to Tarsus. The entire region had become part of the Roman empire, so travel was easier. He had heard Tarsus was a thriving marketplace. It had quickly become an important port along the trade route, and news of its prosperity had spread throughout the empire. My great-grandfather decided business opportunities would be greater there.

My grandfather and father followed in his footsteps and each subsequent generation benefited from the ever-increasing prosperity of their trade. As a result of my father's success, he became influential in our city and a respected leader of our synagogue. Our family enjoyed a modicum of wealth and the prestige that came with it.

I am my parents' firstborn child. My father was elated to have a son to whom he could pass along the traditions and beliefs of our family and our people. It was with great pride that on my eighth day he presented me to the priest to be circumcised. The covenant between Jehovah God and His people would be continued through my father's son. It was a joyous day of celebration for him and for all our extended family!

When I was thirty days old, my father again brought me before the priest. This time he presented his offering of five silver shekels to redeem me as his firstborn son as required under our law.

As soon as I was old enough to walk and talk, my father began teaching me the stories from the Torah. I learned about sin that began with Adam and Eve, and the flood that God brought upon the earth as judgment for the sins of the people. I learned about Abraham, the patriarch of our people, and the substitutionary sacrifice that God provided on top of Mount Moriah to take the place of his son Isaac.

My father taught me how God had provided for His people through Isaac's grandson Joseph, and how He delivered His people from slavery and oppression through Moses. Most of all, he taught me the law that God gave to our people through Moses, because through it we are set apart as His chosen people. Of all the people on earth, we are the only people God calls His own. The laws He has given us are for our protection and to set us apart as His.

I excelled in my studies. The more I learned, the more I desired to know. The more I knew, the prouder I became of my people, our legacy, and our unique relationship with Jehovah God. I knew it was a relationship that must be guarded and protected against anything and anyone who might try to distort or compromise our beliefs and our laws. Even at a young age, I became an impassioned defender of our beliefs.

My father affirmed and stoked that passion. He often reminded me that Moses had written, *"You must commit yourselves wholeheartedly to these commands."*[2] But it was my mother who always reminded me that God had preceded that statement by saying, "*Listen, O Israel! The Lord is our God, the Lord alone. And you must love the Lord your God with all your heart, all your soul, and all your strength.*"[3]

"Saul," she would say, "never forget that first and foremost God seeks your never-ending love. Don't become so single focused on obeying God that you fail to love Him!" Unfortunately, I often lost sight of her counsel.

My sister, Dinah, was born when I was three. As much as I took after my father in appearance and temperament, Dinah resembled our mother. By the time she was three or four years of age, she was already a softening influence in my life – an influence that I would lose sight of far too soon.

Tarsus was a wonderful city in which to grow up. It is situated at the mouth of the Cydnus River as it empties into the beautiful blue waters of the Mediterranean Sea. The summers are very hot, so the river and the sea are an inviting reprieve from the heat of the day – whether it's the water itself or the cool breeze along the shore. The winters can be chilly and damp, but gratefully they are short.

The city is filled with many wonders – stately palaces, burgeoning marketplaces, and the waterworks that date back to the days of the Hittites. It is easy to spot the Roman additions of the baths and fountains that have emerged throughout the city, as well as the sporting stadium built when I was a boy.

As I got older, my parents allowed me to explore the docks along the shore. Tarsus had become quite the international port. Each day I would see ships from all over the world. I would greet the sailors from Macedonia, Greece, Spain, Syria, Judea – and the great ships from Rome. On occasion, I would dream about visiting those shores … but my father would quickly remind me of my God-given responsibility to be a defender of our religious beliefs right here in our own land. I didn't need to be concerned with exploring those Gentile lands, he reminded me. I must keep my attention focused on our people and our purpose.

One of the advantages of growing up in Tarsus was the education I received. Our schools rivaled those of Athens and Alexandria. Tarsus was home to some of the finest minds in the empire. My father wanted me to benefit from a superior education in the sciences, mathematics, and language. The teachings at these Gentile schools, combined with my lessons from the Torah at the feet of our rabbis and my father, prepared me well for the next phase of my education.

When I was fifteen, my father took me to Jerusalem to study under the esteemed teacher Gamaliel. This was a coveted opportunity made available to me only because of my family's position and longstanding history. My father had been a fellow student with Rabbi Gamaliel at the prestigious school of Hillel the elder. Rabbi Hillel had lived to be 120 years old. There were many who compared him to Moses, not only because of his long life, but also because of his wisdom. He had poured his life into his grandson, Gamaliel, with the intention that he would lead the school upon Hillel's death. That transition had already occurred when I started attending the school.

Even the journey to Jerusalem was an educational opportunity. We sailed from Tarsus to Sidon, Syria, and then on to Caesarea Maritima. As we arrived in the port, I looked out over the city in awe. My father explained its history to me.

The puppet king who had been entrusted with the governance of this region of the Roman Empire was Herod the Great. He had done much to fuel the economic development of this region. Most notably, he had built this city of Caesarea Maritima on the coast of the Mediterranean Sea. Development of the city had begun with the construction of a palace built on a promontory (peninsula) that jutted out into the sea. It included a large decorative pool surrounded by a protective portico. It was a majestic sight from the vantage of our ship. I found myself secretly thinking I would like to visit the palace one day to view its splendor. But I quickly put the thought out of my mind.

Herod established the city as a major commercial port by constructing the largest artificial harbor built in the open sea. It was one of the most impressive harbors of the day, and it boasted the region's largest amphitheater and hippodrome. Herod named the city in honor of his patron, Caesar Augustus, who had been emperor at the time. His son Archelaus had inhabited the Caesarean palace for a brief time after his father's death, but his rule was short-lived. Control of this region had since been turned over to a series of Roman governors, known as prefects, with Caesarea serving as the provincial capital.

Valerius Gratus was the current Roman prefect in 20 A.D. when we arrived. He was the fourth prefect to rule over this region, his three predecessors each having served for three years. He was now five years into his rule. He, like his predecessors, had distinguished himself throughout his military career. His was a military appointment and not a political one. His rule of the province thus far had been relatively unremarkable, which meant he did little to gain the attention and favor of Emperor Tiberius or the Jews. But he also did little to warrant their disfavor – with one notable exception.

Gratus knew the true "leader" of the Jewish people is the high priest. The high priest presides over the Great Sanhedrin, the supreme court of the land. Their voices have the greatest influence over what the people think and do – not only religiously, but also socially and politically. Their religious influence even reaches to Tarsus and other Jewish enclaves scattered throughout the empire.

Gratus realized if he could control the high priest, he could better "control" the people. An ambitious and powerful priest by the name of Annas had been the high priest under the three previous prefects, and Gratus feared the overwhelming power Annas wielded over the people.

My father had attended school with Annas and knew him well. He attested to the fact that Annas was an ambitious and treacherous man.

One of Gratus's first actions as a new prefect had been to remove Annas and replace him with a series of his own puppets. Each served as high priest for only one year. Limiting their term limited the power base they were able to establish. But Gratus's interference in the social and religious practice of the Jews did not endear him to the Jewish people.

Three years later, he had succumbed to the pressure of the Jews and named their choice, Caiaphas, as high priest – with the caveat he would only serve a one-year term – or a succession of one-year terms. Though Caiaphas was now firmly seated in the position in his third consecutive one-year term, the people still resented Gratus's pagan interference in their religious practices. This made him reluctant to make any further changes. And Annas had craftily regained his seat of power by arranging for Caiaphas to marry his daughter, making the high priest his son-in-law.

This was my first exposure to learning how power was traded and gained. I knew I had much to learn, but it appeared I would be surrounded by experts in the art of power brokering as I studied in Jerusalem.

My father and I set sail one more time to the port of Jaffa, farther down the coast. I knew from my Scriptural studies that this was the port from which Jonah had set sail on his ill-fated attempt to flee the Lord and disobey His command. I found myself thinking that I had no interest in disobeying the Lord and ending up in the belly of a big fish!

From there, we traveled over land to the city of Jerusalem. I had been so excited as we drew near to the city, but I was shocked by the sight of four men hanging on crosses near the city as we approached from the west. I was aware the Romans used that form of execution, but I had never before seen it firsthand. My father said it was a fairly frequent occurrence here in Jerusalem. I could not imagine what these men had done to prompt such brutal treatment. It momentarily cast a pallor across our otherwise remarkable journey.

But as I looked up, I saw the city walls and remembered that over five hundred years earlier, Nehemiah had led the people to rebuild them. As we stepped through the Damascus Gate into the upper city, we were immediately surrounded by the merchant stalls. It wasn't as colorful as the marketplaces in Tarsus, but it was just as crowded.

My father had promised me we would go directly to the temple before we did anything else. Herod the Great had commissioned a rebuilding of the temple several years earlier, but I had not pictured it as being this grand. It was said that it now rivaled the splendor of the temple as it was originally built by King Solomon.

I realized that with each step we took leading up to the temple mount, I was moving closer to the holy place where Jehovah God dwelt among His people. The air was filled with the sweet aroma of incense mixed with the smell of the sacrifices being offered over roaring flames. Each of the courts of the temple was filled with people coming to present their offerings and sacrifices to God and offer up their prayers and requests for blessing.

Though the city of Jerusalem was much plainer than Tarsus, the temple far outshined anything I had ever seen. I couldn't help but think that Jehovah God must be pleased with His people and our commitment to His laws and commandments. God was truly being glorified in this place – or so I believed.

I saw a group of students who were about my age standing with their teacher in the Court of Men. The teacher was obviously instructing them and quizzing them on their understanding. I wondered if my teacher would be bringing me here as well.

. . .

As we walked by, my father recognized the teacher, so we went over to greet him. As it turned out, God had ordered our steps directly to the spot where Rabbi Gamaliel was teaching the very group I would be joining. My father and teacher decided my instruction would begin immediately! After a brief word of farewell, my father left me with my class and began his journey back home. It would be five years before I would see him again.

I was no longer a student; I was now officially a "talmid." A student wants to know what the teacher knows in order to complete his studies. But a talmid wants to be like the teacher. A talmid wants to become what the teacher is. Quickly, I discovered that every one of us in the group was passionately devoted to Rabbi Gamaliel. We paid attention to not only everything he said but also to everything he did. We not only listened, but we also watched and imitated him so as to become like him. Whenever possible, wherever he went, we went. I will confess to you – I came to love him and respect him, perhaps as much as my father – because he became my spiritual father.

The other talmidim in the group came from a variety of places and from a variety of backgrounds. A few were the sons of rabbis. A few were the sons of members of our Great Sanhedrin. A few were the sons of wealthy merchants and tradesmen, like me.

One of the merchant's sons was a boy named Mnason. He and I were the same age and had a lot in common. His family had moved to Jerusalem from Cyprus when he was a baby, and now his father was a successful weaver in the city. Like my father, his took great pride in knowing his son was being trained by Rabbi Gamaliel. We soon became close friends – a friendship that would last a lifetime.

One of the other talmidim – one who was with us for a short time – was the son of a fisherman. His name was John, and he was from Galilee of all places. I discovered John was related to Elder Hillel through his mother, making Rabbi Gamaliel a distant relative. But his ability to train under Rabbi Gamaliel was not purely the result of his familial relationship – he had a trained mind and an excellent grasp of the Scriptures. Who knew that a fisherman could also be such an outstanding scholar?

Other than Mnason, I can't say I became good friends with any of the other talmidim. There was too much of a collegial competition between us. But we did all grow to respect one another's passion to learn. It was clear that some of us desired to know more about God, and some of us desired to know more about His law. Some of us were more concerned about growing in our love for God and following the spirit of His laws, while others of us were more concerned with the letter of the law and our own ability to rise above others through our strict adherence to it and knowledge of it.

Perhaps said another way, some sought to serve God and others sought to lord our knowledge over the people. I observed that John fell into the former category while Mnason and I, and many others in our group, fell into the latter. Honestly, at the time, I wasn't sure where Rabbi Gamaliel fell – but given his position, I presumed he too fell into the latter.

My five years as a talmid passed swiftly. I could hardly believe when it was time for me to return to Tarsus. But it had been agreed I would return home on my twentieth birthday. I had come to relish being a part of the religious community of Jerusalem. I would miss my days in the temple. I would miss my interaction not only with Rabbi Gamaliel, but also with many of our other leading rabbis and priests – including an occasional conversation with our current high priest, Caiaphas.

It was with a heavy heart that I said goodbye to Mnason and to the city I had come to love and began my journey back home to Tarsus. The journey was uneventful, so I had plenty of time to consider what my life would look like in the days to come. I knew I would one day return to Jerusalem – but I did not know when. Neither did I know all that would welcome me upon my arrival in Tarsus!

* * *

3

I am a Jew and a citizen of Tarsus in Cilicia, which is an important city.[(1)]

* * *

Though I had been in no hurry to leave Jerusalem, I was happy to see the welcoming vista of Tarsus as my ship made its way into harbor. Until that moment, I hadn't realized how much I missed home.

As the captain maneuvered our ship into its berth, I saw my sister waiting on the deck, scanning the horizon expectantly. I couldn't help but notice the pensive look on her face. She had matured into a beautiful young woman during my five-year absence. But I wondered how she knew I would be arriving on this ship … on this day. I quickly gathered my few belongings, conveyed my thanks to the captain, and made my way to my sister.

After a warm greeting and embrace, we began our short trip home. Along the way, Dinah explained that she had been coming to the docks every day for the past week. Our father had known I would be making my way home just as we had agreed. And he knew the last leg of my trip would be by ship from Sidon to Tarsus. So, each day my sister had watched for any ship arriving from Sidon.

"As much as I appreciate that you were at the dock to greet me upon my arrival," I said, "I'm still not clear as to why you needed to do so."

"I came to tell you that father is not well," Dinah replied. "One day, about a month ago, he collapsed. He was burning up with fever. The doctor told us he had contracted Roman fever. It is highly unusual for the disease to be contracted this early in the year, but many of our neighbors have died of it in recent weeks. We have tried every poultice the doctor suggested but to no avail. Each day he gets worse, and we are fairly certain the only reason he is still alive is that he willed himself to live until you returned home.

"Prepare yourself, brother. Father no longer looks like himself. He refuses to eat, and he is merely a bundle of skin and bones. Most days he is very agitated. But mother and I believe he will calm down once he sees you. It is possible he will allow himself to take his last breath once he has seen you."

I was grateful for Dinah's warning because it lessened the shock when I saw my father. My mother seemed relieved to have me home. She wept softly into my shoulder as we embraced. Then she excused herself so my father and I could have some time alone. My father seemed calm, so apparently my presence had made a difference.

He asked me to tell him about my time in Jerusalem. As I recounted my studies, my experiences, and the people I had met, he closed his eyes and smiled. I don't think I realized until that moment how important it was to my father for me to receive that education in Jerusalem. Being a Pharisee had been more important to my father than almost anything else in his life. It was the crowning expression of his devoutness to Jehovah God. He had always believed his own education in the school of Hillel had prepared him to be a "proper" Pharisee. And he had felt my time at the feet of Rabbi

Gamaliel would do the same for me. As my father lay there listening to my stories, he was content that his legacy would be carried on by his son. Now, he could let go.

I don't know how long I had been talking before I realized my father had taken his last breath. As I looked at his still body lying peacefully on his bed, I knew he was dead. I leaned down and kissed him gently on top of his head. He had finished his race!

I gathered my mother and sister back into the room. As the reality of his passing settled into our hearts, there was a mixture of sorrow and relief – knowing he was no longer with us but knowing he was no longer suffering. It was already late in the day, so I knew we needed to act quickly. We buried his body before the sun set as the law of Moses required. The rabbi, together with our many friends and neighbors, took care of all the details. His death had been anticipated, and most of the arrangements had already been made. I knew my mother was grieving his death, but I also knew his illness had taken a toll on her. I turned my attention to consoling her.

I was reminded throughout our days of mourning just how respected my father had been in our community. He had lived righteously. He had honored God and His commandments. He had been a good Pharisee. He had been a good Jew. He had left a clear path for me to walk, and he had left big shoes for me to fill. I was now the patriarch of my family. I was the provider for my mother and sister. I was expected to take over my father's business. It was my job to care for and nurture my family. Any other ambitions I had would need to be put on hold. My family was now my responsibility.

The day after my father died, Dinah introduced me to a young man named Reuben. The two of them were the same age, and he clearly had his eye on my sister. He had recently become an apprentice to my father. Truth be told, during the last few weeks of my father's life, Reuben had managed to keep my father's business functioning. Our family owed him many thanks. Though he would now become my apprentice, I knew in many ways he would be the teacher and I would be the student. Once shiva (the first seven days of mourning) had passed, I joined Reuben in our tent-making shop. Though I had not been in the shop for over five years, very little had changed.

Tarsian tents are renowned throughout the Roman Empire for their high quality. The Tarsus mountains, located 40 kilometers to the north of our city, are the home to huge herds of black goats. Their hair is shorn, much in the way a sheep's wool is shaved off. The hair is then woven into a strong cloth called cilicium, which is used for a variety of applications that will withstand heavy use and wear – such as floor coverings, cloaks, and tents. Because of its natural black color, our fabric does not need to be dyed. Our black tents are used by caravans, nomads, and armies throughout Asia and Syria.

Because of my family's Roman citizenship, we have one other advantage over other tentmakers. Tarsus was designated a free city by Caesar Augustus during my great-grandfather's lifetime. At that time, the Roman Empire had just put down a great rebellion that had arisen as the empire was transitioning from a monarchy to a republic. Tarsian citizens had aided Augustus and the conservative opposition in their fight.

To the victor comes the spoils. Being a free city means Roman soldiers are not stationed within our gates. We select our own magistrates and local council to govern the administrative affairs of our city. Having just returned from Jerusalem and the conspicuous oppression of Roman rule in that city, it made me even more grateful for our designation.

But even though Tarsus is a free city, that doesn't mean all Tarsians are Roman citizens. Even the Roman republic has a class system, and that system requires that anyone born outside of Rome itself must be born into a family of social standing over at least four generations. My father was the fourth generation. It was because of what he achieved – and the generations before him – that my father, and now I, enjoy the distinction of being a Roman citizen.

. . .

There are many advantages to citizenship. One of them is we are exempt from paying taxes, including the duty taxes on anything we buy or sell. That means my family enjoys a competitive advantage in the sale of our tents.

As I walked through the streets of Tarsus, I was struck by how much it had grown while I was gone. People were being drawn from all over the empire in search of the prosperity found in our city. Though we were less than half the size of Jerusalem, we enjoyed good roads, good public health systems, and the kind of city beautification I had witnessed in Caesarea Maritima.

There was no question that the quality of life in Tarsus was better than that of Jerusalem and most of Judea. But I will confess that something – or Someone – was calling me back to Jerusalem. There was a tug on my heart. However, I knew my current responsibilities meant I needed to put any plans to follow my heart on hold … at least for now.

One of the things I enjoyed most about being home was reconnecting with friends – particularly Arsakes, Ashmus, and Benjamin. The four of us were all the same age and had enjoyed a friendship that dated back to when we were youngsters. We had met at school. We came from very different families and backgrounds, but we shared a common bond. Each of us was our parents' only son and expected to carry on the tradition of our family. We had no brothers with whom to play, with whom to argue, with whom to compete, or with whom to confide. So, despite our many dissimilarities, we became brothers to one another. Our bond became what we had in common – and, for a time, that was stronger than any of our differences.

Arsakes was our informal leader whenever we were together. His father was one of our city's magistrates, elected to successive one-year terms by the citizens of our city. He never received any compensation for his supervision of the public works of our city, but he wielded great influence and power. Arsakes mirrored his father's ability to lead and influence people. He taught me how to remain steadfast in my conviction even when others are against me.

Ashmus was the son of one of the stoic philosophers in our city. Stoic philosophy, which originated with the Greeks, is a philosophy of personal ethics informed by logical thought. Stoics believe the path to happiness is found in accepting the moment as it presents itself and by resisting the distracting desire for pleasure or the fear of pain. They believe everything is rooted in nature, so to live a good life you must follow the natural order. Ashmus was a diligent student of his father's teachings. Though we believe very different things, I have always enjoyed the intellectual stimulation of our debates. He taught me how to communicate my beliefs in a clear and logical manner.

Benjamin is the son of one of our rabbis. His father is a Sadducee, so though we share a common faith, we differ on many of the theological tenets. Like most Sadducees, Benjamin's beliefs have been too greatly influenced by the Greek stoics, and they are much less conservative than those of us who are Pharisees. But he inspired me to diligently study to show myself approved.

Arsakes and Ashmus are Gentiles. Benjamin and I are, of course, Jews. Many of my Pharisee brothers look down on me for having Gentile – and Sadducee – friends. But I know our bond goes much deeper. We remain committed to one another and know we can always count on each other for help and support. Each of these men demonstrated that support as I walked through the pain of my father's death.

King Solomon once wrote, *"As iron sharpens iron, so a friend sharpens a friend."*[(2)] God used these men in that way in my life. Through Arsakes, He taught me how to lead others. Through Ashmus, He taught me how to debate and clearly communicate truth. Through Benjamin, He taught me to go deeper in my understanding of the truths I believe. And I pray that God has used me to influence their lives as well.

. . .

Four years after my father died, Reuben asked my permission to marry my sister. His request was not a surprise; as a matter of fact, I had been expecting him to come to me for some time. Throughout our time working together, he had proven to be a man on whom I could depend. He had demonstrated his love for Jehovah God, as well as his love for my sister. He had shown me he would always care for her. And I knew Dinah loved him and respected him. So, without any reservation, I gave my permission and rejoiced with them.

One year later, we celebrated their marriage. As my wedding present to them, I made Reuben a partner in our family's business. Our business had prospered since my father's passing, and to a great degree that was because of Reuben's efforts. I was grateful to God for bringing him into our lives.

Ten months after their marriage, Dinah gave birth to a son they named Hezron, which means "the first to sprout." He indeed would be the first – with three more following him. Our mother found great joy in being a grandmother, and it gave her a renewed zest for life and a sense of purpose. Regrettably, she would only meet one of her grandchildren. Three years after Hezron was born, our mother died as the result of a plague that passed through our city.

During my nine years back in Tarsus, I had seen and experienced a lot of change. Both my parents were dead. My sister was married and blessed with a growing family. My brother-in-law was well prepared to lead our family business. I knew God was now leading me to return to Jerusalem. I no longer had the responsibilities that brought me back to Tarsus and kept me there. God was giving me an opportunity to passionately serve Him alongside the chief priests of our faith.

I had heard about a Man named Jesus who claimed to be the Son of God. He had performed many miracles and people had begun to believe He was the promised Messiah. But the high priest and leading council disagreed. They saw Him as disrespectful of the authority given them by the law of Moses. They considered Him a deceiver and a blasphemer. They accused Him of being sent by Beelzebub. It had taken them a while, but eventually they had convinced the Roman governor to crucify Him on that same hill where I had often seen crosses near the Jerusalem gates.

But apparently, His followers had secretly moved His body from the tomb in which He had been buried. They were claiming He had risen from the dead. As a Pharisee, I believe in the resurrection of the dead. But that will occur one day when God returns. The chief priests adamantly denied this claim of His resurrection. And who were we to trust – a carpenter from Nazareth with no formal religious training or the chief priests placed in leadership over His people by Jehovah God? I had also heard that a group of His followers who called themselves The Way believed Jesus was alive. They were leading many Jews astray with this falsehood.

Men were needed who would eradicate this abomination against God and His law. Men were needed who would be defenders of the faith and crusaders for truth. The time had come for those to stand up and fight the good fight. And I knew I was to be one of those men.

Everything in my life pointed to that destiny. I must return without delay. So, one month after we buried my mother, I left Tarsus and headed back to Jerusalem.

* * *

4

His accusers took off their coats and laid them at the feet of a young man named Saul.[1]

* * *

It wasn't long before I sensed a change had taken place in Jerusalem since I was last there. As planned, I went straight to the temple upon my arrival. I found a large group gathered on the eastern side of the temple's outer court in the covered portico called Solomon's Porch. I had never seen such large groups gathered there before. Teaching always took place in the outer courts. But this crowd was intently listening to two men who were taking turns addressing the crowd.

I decided to get closer so I could hear what they were saying. The more animated of the two was big and burly. He looked like a man who had spent most of his life working outdoors with his hands. I later learned he was a fisherman. The other man was much younger. I soon recognized him as John – the Galilean who had briefly been one of the other talmidim with me studying under Rabbi Gamaliel. He had demonstrated an excellent grasp of the Scriptures, but due to his brief time in study was not considered a trained teacher. He was simply an ordinary man, which I presumed was also true of his companion. What gave either of these men the right to teach in the porch of the temple?

Just then I saw two men carrying a third man who appeared to be lame. They carried the afflicted man into the center of the crowd and set him down before John and the other man. The bigger man looked at the lame man and said, *"Look at us!"*(2) The lame man looked up at them expectantly. *"In the name of Jesus Christ the Nazarene, get up and walk!"*(3)

I was shocked! They were invoking the name of the One whom the high priests had declared to be a blasphemer. And they were doing so right here outside of the temple. How was this heresy being permitted?

But as those thoughts quickly passed through my mind, I saw the lame man jump to his feet! He began to walk, then he began to leap. The friends who had carried him began to jump and shout with him. "Glory to God – and praise be to His Son, Jesus Christ the Nazarene!" they shouted. Soon the entire crowd lifted their voices with them.

I could not believe my ears ... or my eyes. Surely this had all been contrived by the followers of The Way. And obviously John and his companion were part of that deception!

The big man spoke up. *"Through faith in the name of Jesus, this man was healed – and you know how crippled he was before. Faith in Jesus' name has healed him before your very eyes. Repent of your sins and turn to God, so that your sins may be wiped away."*(4)

Others who were watching from the Women's Court began to move toward the porch. They were being drawn by the miracle they had witnessed and the words they heard.

• • •

I knew I had to find the high priest Caiaphas and Rabbi Gamaliel. Surely, they would not allow this blasphemy to take place – in and around the temple no less. Were they not aware of the heresy being spoken here with such boldness? I set off in earnest to the Hall of Hewn Stones, the meeting place of the Great Sanhedrin, in order to find them.

When I entered the hall, I immediately spotted Caiaphas and Annas. They were having a private conversation in a corner of the room. I approached slowly and respectfully – but I would not be put off from my mission. Both men turned and looked at me. "Saul, it is good to see you have returned to Jerusalem," Caiaphas said.

I was honored the high priest recognized me, let alone remembered my name! However, Annas gave me an impatient look, clearly letting me know I had interrupted their important conversation.

From another corner of the room, I saw Rabbi Gamaliel approaching us. He smiled as he called out, "If it isn't one of my most dedicated talmidim! Welcome, Saul! We have missed you."

Rabbi Gamaliel's appearance seemed to set Annas somewhat at ease. Gamaliel asked about my father, and I shared about his death. We asked about one another's families, and then I turned the conversation to what I had witnessed when I arrived.

"It is a blight upon our land, and a perversion of all we believe," Annas declared. "We thought we had taken care of that interloper once and for all. But where One died, hundreds, if not thousands, have now sprung forth! If Pilate had not become so soft after the crucifixion of Jesus, we could have crucified His handful of followers and been done with this! But Pilate did not have the courage to do what needed to be done!"

• • •

Caiaphas spoke up. "We have arrested the two principal leaders – Peter, as well as John, the distant cousin of Gamaliel and Annas – on several occasions. But our actions seem to make them bolder. And we risk Roman retribution if we take matters into our own hands."

"That Galilean fisherman John is no cousin of mine!" Annas retorted. "At least, one for whom I will make any claim!"

"A while back," Gamaliel interjected, "I reminded the council of two other movements that began among the people that soon came to nothing. I told them *my advice is to leave these men alone. Let them go. If they are planning and doing these things merely on their own, it will soon be overthrown. But if it is from God, you will not be able to overthrow them. You may even find yourselves fighting against God!*"(5)

"And yet, their numbers increase each day," Annas said. "Something must be done!"

"I believe Jehovah God has led me to return to Jerusalem to help you eliminate this threat to our laws and our way of life," I said. "Allow me to formulate a plan as to what needs to be done, and I will bring it to you for your approval."

"The high council cannot be implicated in any way," Caiaphas said, "or Pilate will have us all arrested. Whatever you do must appear to be a response of the people themselves."

"I understand," I replied. "I will bring a plan to you within a few days!"

Annas and Caiaphas both nodded approvingly. However, Gamaliel remained silent and looked at me cautiously. I bade the men farewell and went off to find my friend Mnason. I was confident he would let me stay with him.

After dinner that evening, Mnason and I spoke about the followers of The Way. "I was in the streets on the Day of Pentecost four years ago," he told me, "when we all began to hear a sound like a mighty windstorm. A large crowd of us went to see what was going on. There were people from many lands in the crowd. Suddenly, the men who had been followers of Jesus began to speak, and everyone in the crowd heard their words in their own native language. We marveled! How could these uneducated Galileans speak to us in such a way? Saul, I do not understand what happened that day, but I can tell you that Jerusalem has not been the same since."

The next day I decided to find John and speak with him. Perhaps I could reason with him. I went to the only place I knew I may find him – Solomon's Porch. When I arrived, his companion, whom I now knew to be Peter, was speaking to the crowd again. It appeared there were more than just two of them teaching. I was able to identify at least ten other men who were also providing leadership to the group.

They appeared to be redistributing food and money that had been brought by those who were able. They were sharing it with those in need. I had to admit there was a different spirit among this group. They didn't seem to be giving because they had to in obedience to a law; they seemed to be giving with joy.

Just then I saw John and caught his eye. He immediately walked over and embraced me. I had forgotten John was a hugger!

"Saul, my friend, how have you been?" he asked. His demeanor took me off guard. I momentarily forgot he was one of the key leaders of a movement threatening our way of life. Instead, we talked like two former schoolmates catching up after being apart for a long time. But soon, I regained my sense of purpose and redirected the conversation.

• • •

"John, why are you, of all people, leading your fellow Jews to turn from following our religious leaders and instead follow this One who was put to death for His blasphemy?" I asked. "You know the Scriptures as well as I do. How have you been so deceived?"

"It's because I know the Scriptures, I know Jesus is in fact the Promised One," John replied. "I knew it from the first day I met Him eight years ago. He is the One of whom the prophets foretold. He is the One who John the baptizer told us to watch for. He is the Son of God who always has been. *In the beginning the Word already existed. The Word was with God, and the Word was God. He existed in the beginning with God. God created everything through Him, and nothing was created except through Him. The Word gave life to everything that was created, and His life brought light to everyone. Then the Word became human and made His home among us. He was full of unfailing love and faithfulness. And we have seen His glory, the glory of the Father's One and only Son.*"[(6)]

"But John, He's dead!" I interrupted. "How can the Son of God be dead? He was a man like any other. Perhaps He could perform miracles, but even demons can do that! How can you continue to follow a dead imposter?"

"But He's not dead!" John declared. "On the third day after His death on the cross, He rose from the tomb. Many of us who are here in this place saw Him, spoke with Him, and ate with Him after He arose. He defeated death, Saul! He defeated sin and the grave! He made the way once and for all for our sins to be forgiven! Then He returned to heaven to sit at the right hand of the Father.

"He is the substitutionary Lamb that God promised our patriarch Abraham many years ago on top of Mount Moriah. He is the Passover Lamb who has saved us through His shed blood! *He is the Alpha and Omega, the First and the Last, the Beginning and the End.*"[(7)]

• • •

"John, you are deceived!" I shouted. "You have been blinded to the truth. If you continue on like this, you will die. The high council will have you crucified just like your Teacher."

"If I must die," John replied, "then I will rejoice that God has counted me worthy to suffer death for the name of Jesus. Saul, I too was once blind, but now I see! I pray that God by His grace will allow your eyes to be opened so you too can truly see!

"Seek Him, Saul, with all of your heart, and you will find Him!"

With that, John returned to the others and left me there to ponder what he said. I would most definitely seek Jehovah God – I would seek Him to find out what He would have me do to eradicate this threat to all I believed and held holy! If these people counted it a privilege to be martyred for what they believed, perhaps we could most happily oblige them!

In the few days I had been back in the city, reports were coming in daily that more and more people were abandoning their Jewish heritage and becoming followers of Jesus. Even priests were turning to The Way. Time was of the essence! It would take bold action to turn this tide! It would take a bold leader! I believed God had chosen me to be that leader – and a plan was formulating in my mind!

I had heard Caiaphas clearly when he said the high council could not be implicated in any way. Those involved would need to be foreigners but also passionately devoted Jews. I was familiar with the Synagogue of the Freedmen in the city. It was made up of men from Cyrene, Alexandria, parts of Asia, and my own birthplace, Cilicia. Most of these men were Jews who, either themselves or their families before them, had been freed by their Roman masters and had chosen to return to Jerusalem.

• • •

I had become acquainted with Theodatus Vettenus, the chief priest of the synagogue, during my time of study here in the city. His family had lived in Tarsus until he was a boy, when they relocated to Jerusalem. His son, Junius, was about my age. I had visited the synagogue on several occasions during my previous stay and had enjoyed the spirited debate of the Scriptures in my native Roman tongue. Though I did not agree with some of the Hellenistic influence on their views, I admired their passion and commitment to the Torah and Talmud. I knew I could count on them to become allies in my effort – and I was right!

Since Peter and John had previously been brought before the high council, I knew any effort directed toward them would be seen as further action taken by the high priest. I also knew the movement would be strengthened by any attempt to punish the two of them – just as it had been by the crucifixion of their Savior. So, I decided to target some of their "lesser" leaders.

I learned the "believers" – as they called themselves – had recently selected a group of men to make certain the Hellenistic widows who were converts to their faith were receiving adequate care and food. I told Junius and some of the other young men this effort was being undertaken to draw more Hellenistic Jews to the ranks of The Way. These widows were being blinded by the promise of free food, similar to the way the Nazarene had drawn many when He too fed the multitudes. As I anticipated, this only angered the young men more toward these followers of Jesus.

One of those chosen to serve the widows was a man named Stephen. Supposedly, he had displayed amazing miracles and signs among the people, similar to those of Peter and John. He was beginning to gain notoriety, but he was not yet one of their prominent leaders. I decided he would be the one we would target first.

I watched and learned his daily routine. I remembered hearing that the high priest had arranged for the arrest of Jesus to occur out of the view of a crowd. I decided we would follow a similar course of action with Stephen.

• • •

One morning, I, together with Junius and several other young men, found Stephen in the city. As we had arranged, I watched from a distance as Junius approached Stephen saying, "I hear you are one of the followers of the Man who was crucified – Jesus the Nazarene."

Stephen nodded. Junius continued. "We understand Jesus taught that He would destroy the temple and change the customs handed down to us from Moses. How can you – a Jew – believe such blasphemy?" The other men then began to surround Stephen.

To his credit, Stephen remained calm as he responded. He reminded me of how Rabbi Gamaliel would patiently and deftly answer the questions we talmidim would pose in our feeble attempts to stump him. Each question Junius and the others asked was met with eloquent and thoughtful answers that pointed to the writings of the prophets. Stephen was clearly more knowledgeable of the Scriptures than his questioners. It quickly became obvious he was not going to be intimidated by this group.

But suddenly, as we had prearranged, some of the young men began to shout, "*We just heard you blaspheme Moses … and even God!*"[(8)] On cue, I walked forward to approach the men as did several others whom I had arranged to wait nearby. Three temple guards also quickly appeared in our midst.

Junius turned to us and pled his case that this "follower of The Way" was speaking blasphemy in the street. "He must be taken before the high council!" Junius exclaimed. We all nodded our heads in agreement. The guards took hold of Stephen, and we began our short journey to the Hall of Hewn Stones. Everything was going according to plan.

That was, until we arrived at the hall. Caiaphas convened the council and Junius, together with the other witnesses, stated their false charges and accusations. But suddenly, every head turned to look at Stephen. His face had begun to shine as brightly as an angel's. Momentarily, no one knew what to do – we just stared. Then Caiaphas looked at Stephen, took control of the situation, and asked, *"Are these accusations true?"*(9)

Stephen was no more intimidated by the high priest or the high council than he had been by Junius and the other young men. He respectfully began to answer the charge against him by walking us all through our history beginning with Abraham. He recounted the faithfulness of God to each generation – even when we, as a people, had been faithless.

But then, while taking time to look at us individually, he said:

"The Most High doesn't live in temples made by human hands. As the prophet says, 'Heaven is My throne, and the earth is My footstool. Could you build Me a temple as good as that?' asks the Lord. 'Could you build Me such a resting place? Didn't My hands make both heaven and earth?'

"You stubborn people! You are heathen at heart and deaf to the truth. Must you forever resist the Holy Spirit? That's what your ancestors did, and so do you! Name one prophet your ancestors didn't persecute! They even killed the ones who predicted the coming of the Righteous One – the Messiah whom you betrayed and murdered. You deliberately disobeyed God's law, even though you received it from the hands of angels."(10)

The religious leaders were infuriated. Who was this man to make these accusations against them? They began to shout and shake their fists at Stephen. Caiaphas and Annas placed their hands over their ears and shouted to drown out his voice.

Stephen, however, remained unflustered and turned his gaze toward heaven. Even as the religious leaders continued to shout, I heard him say, *"Look, I see the heavens opened and the Son of Man standing in the place of honor at God's right hand!"*(11) And every one of us knew he was talking about Jesus!

. . .

I looked at Caiaphas and he nodded. I signaled all of those who had brought Stephen before the council to join me in taking him out. We dragged him through the streets of the city and out through the Damascus Gate. We stopped within eyesight of the place where Jesus had been crucified.

"If he wants to be a follower of Jesus, let him follow Jesus to his death!" I said.

The guards instructed their prisoner to get down on his knees. As he did, the rest of the men took off their outer coats and laid them at my feet before picking up the rocks they would use to stone him. Junius threw the first rock, then the others began to throw theirs without mercy.

As I watched this man die with the same calm demeanor he had answered his accusers, I heard him say, *"Lord, don't charge them with this sin!"*(12) A few moments later, he took his last breath.

I confess that at that moment, I admired this man. He had faced death with a courage and peace beyond anything I had ever witnessed. I'm a Pharisee. I believe in the resurrection of the dead. But this man clearly died believing he was stepping directly from this world into the presence of God. I knew I was on the side of what was right. I was defending the laws passed down to us from Moses. I was purging our land of these blasphemous lies that were being spread. And yet, I didn't know what to make of what I had just witnessed.

I shook off the feeling and pronounced the man dead. I told my companions to return to their homes. Our work was done. We would leave the body for the animals to feast on – or so I said. Those who have committed an offense punishable by death are unclean. They are not to be given a proper burial.

. . .

I never looked back as I walked away. But I knew the other followers of Jesus would not allow Stephen's body to be devoured by animals. I was certain they would secretly come and bury him – and as they did, it would force them to consider their own fate.

I returned to the temple to report the news of Stephen's death. Caiaphas and Annas commended me for my excellent work. They told me I was just the man they had been waiting for. They assured me I would earn an important position of leadership within the high council. I would be greatly rewarded – by man and by God. Together we would purge our land of this scourge once and for all! They commissioned me to assemble a group of men to go from house to house, dragging the followers of The Way to jail. I was to show no mercy. Jehovah God would go before me … or so they said.

As I left the hall, I encountered my teacher, Gamaliel. But something had changed. He no longer looked at me with pride. It had been replaced with sadness and disappointment. And I found I could no longer look him in the eye. His earlier words began to echo in my ears, *"You may even find yourselves fighting against God!"*[13]

My sense of pride and accomplishment suddenly disappeared.

5

I am not even worthy to be called an apostle after the way I persecuted God's church.[1]

* * *

As I returned to my lodgings at Mnason's home that night, I told him what had occurred. He said the streets were already buzzing with the news of Stephen's death. Many of the Jews were saying it was about time these followers of the Nazarene were getting what they deserved for leading the people astray. The gatherings of the followers of The Way had suddenly become less visible. They appeared to now be meeting in secret. Based upon Mnason's reaction, I could not tell if he agreed with what I was doing or not.

I decided we would continue to target the group of men who had been selected to serve alongside Stephen. The next on my list was Parmenas. My spies said he was one of the men who had buried Stephen's body and told me where he was lodging.

. . .

Before the sun rose the next morning, I arrived at his door with the men I had selected and the three temple guards who had been assigned to me. Though we obviously woke him, our arrival did not seem to startle or frighten Parmenas. As rehearsed, I turned to one of the men with me and asked if this was the man he had heard speaking blasphemy against the law of Moses – and even about God. He confirmed Parmenas was the man.

We no longer felt the need to go through the motions of a trial before the council. The Roman authorities appeared satisfied to look the other way. They considered these to be religious disputes not requiring their intervention. Pontius Pilate also seemed willing to let the Jews kill off a few other Jews who were not principal leaders. The men who were with me would serve as the witnesses, the judges, and the executioners.

Without anyone to protest our actions, we dragged Parmenas to the same place we had stoned Stephen. Junius again threw the first stone before he was joined by the other men. Within a matter of minutes, Parmenas had stepped into the presence of his Lord. It struck me that Parmenas never directed one word of fear or hatred toward any of us. He had simply gazed up into heaven as he was being stoned to death. But I found my heart had grown more callous this time. Just as we had done the day before, we left his body to be buried by his fellow followers after we departed.

Obviously, we were going to put down this threat on our religious beliefs and our way of life without any resistance. I wondered why Caiaphas and Annas had allowed so much time to pass before acting. It confirmed to me that God must have truly appointed me for this role. Perhaps I would soon be the high priest!

The next person on our list was Nicolas of Antioch. He was a Gentile who had converted to the Jewish faith. It was hard to believe any Jew would abandon his faith and turn to these lies. I found myself questioning why anyone who had made a conscious decision to join our faith would so easily abandon it. But perhaps that was the answer – he could be convinced to change his beliefs by the most compelling story he was being told at the time.

When we arrived at his door, he was expecting us. But unlike Parmenas, he was obviously unnerved by our appearance. To this point, I had been impressed by the dedication and resolve of these followers of The Way. Though I hated their blasphemy, I had admired their sense of conviction. But Nicolas quickly demonstrated the opposite.

When my "witness" expressed his accusations, Nicolas quickly denied them and began to revise his beliefs about Jesus. He told us Jesus was a great teacher like many of the Greek philosophers who had shaped his own belief system. He also questioned whether Jesus had risen from the dead; but he believed His teachings of loving God and loving your neighbor aligned with the teachings of the Torah and the Talmud.

He adamantly denied believing Jesus was the only Son of God. In his view, we were all "sons" of God. The more he spoke, the more apparent it became we did not need to stone him. His teachings would do more to confuse adherents of The Way. He would be a far greater help to our cause alive than he would dead. He would help sow seeds of disbelief in the movement. I told him not to tell anyone about our visit, and I was certain he would not. He would have had difficulty explaining why we did not stone him as we had the others.

News continued to spread fast about the stonings of Stephen and Parmenas. We soon learned that our other four intended targets had left Jerusalem. I later learned that Philip went to Samaria, Procorus to Seleucia, Nicanor to Damascus, and Timon to Cilicia. At first, I was delighted these men had fled to escape punishment. But as the weeks passed, it became apparent their departure had done more to strengthen the movement beyond Jerusalem.

• • •

Wherever those four and the many other followers scattered, they spread their beliefs. Many people were being healed in their wake, and demons were being cast out. The number of new believers was multiplying. It was as if someone was orchestrating a strategy to reach Jews all over the world!

It seemed the more we did in Jerusalem to put down the movement, the more it grew elsewhere. And it bothered me that the twelve men who were called the apostles of Jesus – including Peter and John – were not the ones spreading the word. Any thought we had about stoning or punishing those twelve was pointless. They were not driving the growth of the movement. They were keeping a low profile in Jerusalem as the message spread.

My periodic meetings with Caiaphas and Annas were becoming less congratulatory. They were concerned things were getting worse instead of better. I must admit that Gamliel's words were again ringing in my ears: *"You may even find yourselves fighting against God!"*[2]

Within a few short months, we heard reports that many people in the city of Sebaste in Samaria were being baptized into their newfound faith. We honestly had little concern about Samaritans, but the word of how this movement was spreading did worry us. The temple in Jerusalem was the center of all we believed and held to be true. The religious leaders in Jerusalem were the shepherds and leaders of our faith. But adherents to this movement were no longer loyal to the temple and the religious leaders. The threat Caiaphas and Annas had felt when Jesus was alive was now becoming an ever-increasing reality since His crucifixion.

I soon found out Peter and John had traveled to Samaria to witness firsthand what was happening there. But they weren't the catalysts of the movement – they were merely observers – and eventually they returned to Jerusalem. Apparently, the evangelist Philip had been the one who initially carried the witness there. And now he was traveling up along the coast of the Mediterranean Sea from Azotus to Caesarea Maritima via Jaffa, preaching about Jesus. Word was beginning to spread out of control!

• • •

I realized we could no longer continue to fight this movement in the same way. We weren't going to stop it by staying in Jerusalem. We needed to get ahead of it. We needed to go to some of the farthest points and stop it from spreading. Then as we crushed the movement at its outside edges, we could gradually make our way back to Jerusalem for the final blow.

Word reached us that Nicanor and others had made their way to Damascus. I decided we would stop the movement from there. It would take me about two weeks to get there so I decided to leave immediately. I presented my plan to Caiaphas and Annas, and they agreed. They provided me with letters of introduction for the religious leaders in Damascus requesting their cooperation. They instructed me to bring Nicanor and the other men and women who had fled Jerusalem back in chains. Word of their arrest and return to Jerusalem would strike fear in the hearts of the apostles and others who had run. It would be the equivalent of a victorious army returning with its defeated captives.

Mnason's eyes betrayed his sadness when I told him I was leaving for Damascus the next morning. Though he was obviously not a follower of The Way, it was clear he did not agree with what was being done to them. In a candid moment, he had said to me, "Were the religious leaders right? Was Jesus truly a deceiver who deserved to die, or was He who He said He was? And if He was, we should not be persecuting His followers, we should be joining them!"

As I was leaving, he said to me, "Saul, I will pray God shows you very clearly on this journey what He would have you do."

We made the journey in haste. The sooner we arrived in Damascus, the sooner we would be able to complete our mission. As each day passed, Junius and the others in my charge became more boisterous and confident about what they believed would be our overwhelming success. They began asking how the religious leaders might reward them for their efforts. Surely, the high priest would be financially generous. After all, we were shutting down a serious threat to their way of life. I was afraid my compatriots were becoming more mercenary in their pursuit and less concerned with our higher purpose of purging this deceit from among our people.

We could just barely see Damascus coming into view on our last day of travel, when suddenly a bright light appeared and shone down on us. It blinded me, and I fell to the ground. I heard a voice say, *"Saul! Saul! Why are you persecuting Me?"*(3)

I could not imagine what was happening or who was speaking. But I knew this was no ordinary event. *"Who are you, sir?"*(4) I asked.

And the voice replied, *"I am Jesus, the One you are persecuting! Now get up and go into the city, and you will be told what you are to do."*(5)

At first, Junius and the other men were speechless. They had apparently seen the light, but it had not affected them. They began to whisper that they had heard someone's voice, but they could not understand what was said. They also had not seen anyone.

I could hear the fear in their voices as they tried to figure out what had just happened. I stood to my feet to retake control of the group, but I dared not move. I could not see the men. For that matter, I could not see anything! The light had left me blind!

I called out to Junius to come help me. He and the other men quickly realized I could not see. Panic began to set in. What were we to do? The men were asking if the words of Rabbi Gamaliel were coming true. I regretted having told them he said, *"You may even find yourselves fighting against God!"*(6) Now they were asking if Jehovah God was fighting against us!

. . .

"What did the voice say to you?" Junius asked.

I was hesitant to answer. I still had too many questions myself, and I knew I would be unable to explain what had happened. So, I told him I wasn't completely sure. That seemed to satisfy him for the moment.

But if the men had not been frightened before, the uncertainty of my answer caused them to be even more fearful! Junius and the others agreed to help me get to the city, but then they would leave. They were not going to risk *fighting against God* any longer! Junius took me by the hand and led me the rest of the way.

We had planned to stay in the home of a merchant named Judas, to whom I had sold tents in the city of Damascus. He had spent time in my home in Tarsus, and I knew I could trust him with the confidentiality of our mission. Even now that my plans had changed, I still knew I could trust him. The voice – if it really was Jesus – had said, *"You will be told what you are to do."*[(7)] I had no idea how that would happen … but I was certain it *would* happen!

We found our way to Straight Street and soon arrived at Judas's home. He welcomed me graciously with genuine concern. I told him about the bright light that had blinded me on the road. I decided not to tell him about the voice I had heard. I explained I just needed some time to rest my eyes in order for my eyesight to return. In the meantime, my companions would be returning to Jerusalem.

I instructed Junius to report to Caiaphas about the blinding light when he arrived in Jerusalem. I told him I would send further word once all of this was sorted out in the next few days. He and the others seemed relieved to be excused from any additional responsibility and departed quickly.

. . .

Judas was a cordial host. He provided me with a room and would have fed me, but I was determined to enter into a fast. I was still uncertain about what had happened. I decided if the voice truly was Jesus and He is the Son of God, I needed to go without food and water to prepare myself for what He would next tell me. And if the voice was not Jesus, I needed to clearly hear from Jehovah God. So I did all I knew to do – I fasted and prayed and called out to God.

Three days passed and I remained in darkness. At the end of that time, there was a knock on my door. Judas quietly announced, "Saul, you have a visitor who has come searching for you."

No one – other than those who had sent me from Jerusalem, my travel companions who were now returning to Jerusalem, and Judas – knew I was here. No one would know to seek me out. But I was expecting this visitor. The night before, God had given me a vision. He had shown me a man named Ananias would come lay his hands on me so I could see again.

My visitor entered the room, but he waited for Judas to close the door and leave before he said anything. I spoke first, asking, "Are you Ananias?" My question seemed to confirm to him what he was supposed to do.

He placed his hands on me – one on each side of my head – and said, *"Brother Saul, the Lord Jesus, who appeared to you on the road, has sent me so that you might regain your sight and be filled with the Holy Spirit."*(8)

Instantly my sight returned! It was as if scales fell from my eyes. I could see the dim light in the room, and I could see Ananias standing before me.

"Saul," Ananias said, "I feared coming to see you. Word had reached us you were coming to arrest every believer in the city. But the Lord told me, *'Go, for Saul is My chosen instrument to take My message to the Gentiles and to kings, as well as to the people of Israel. I will show him how much he must suffer for My name's sake.'*[9] So I came in obedience to our Lord's command.

Any doubt I had about the voice belonging to Jesus disappeared. I knew by His grace, He had stopped me from my intended mission; and by His mercy, He had forgiven me. At that moment, I surrendered myself to Him – the very One I now knew Stephen had been seeing when He gazed into heaven and took his last breath.

I turned to Ananias – who was now my brother – and said, "I must be baptized!" He led me from the house to a pool where he baptized me as a follower of Jesus. Not only had the scales been removed from my eyes, but the weight of sin had been removed from my heart! And the power of the Holy Spirit came upon me.

We returned to Judas's home where he fed us. As he did, I told him about Jesus – and all He had done for me … and for him! Before the sun set, I had the joy of baptizing Judas as another new follower of our Lord and Savior, Jesus Christ!

* * *

6

Instead, I went away into Arabia, and later I returned to the city of Damascus.(1)

* * *

My plans had radically changed! I had come to Damascus to arrest the followers of Jesus. But instead, by the grace of God, I had *become* one of those followers. My plans to stay in Damascus for a while had now been turned upside down. The men I had come here to arrest I now needed to seek for encouragement. I had much to learn, and those who would teach me were frightened of me.

Judas graciously told me I could stay with him for as long as I liked. He also wanted to learn more about Jesus and what it meant to be His follower. Ananias agreed to stay with us for a few days. We bombarded him with questions that first night until he could no longer keep his eyes open. We reluctantly let him get some rest.

After Judas had gone off to do the same, I returned to my room and began to pray. I asked God to show me what He would have me do next. I needed the same kind of clarity He had given me earlier when He spoke to me about Ananias.

When Ananias and Judas awoke the next morning, I asked Ananias to arrange a meeting for me with Nicanor and the other leaders of The Way here in Damascus. I saw Ananias hesitate. I knew he was pondering a very reasonable question: was my conversion genuine, or was it a ploy to uncover the leaders I had come to arrest? I trusted that God would give him – and them – the assurance He was sending me to them.

Later that morning, Ananias returned to tell me Nicanor had agreed to meet with me – but only him. It was obvious the leaders were wisely exercising an abundance of caution, which I agreed was appropriate. Ananias took me to an open area outside the city walls that afternoon along the Amana River. I could tell Nicanor was not taking any chances. An open area would allow him to clearly see if this was a trap. If it were my intention to arrest him, there was no place for my men to wait in hiding.

I could see the apprehension on Nicanor's face as we approached. I had led the men who stoned two of his closest friends to death and arrested and persecuted many others since he had left Jerusalem. He knew I had come to Damascus to do the same thing to him and the other leaders. I had declared them to be my enemy and had committed my life to defeating them. And now, here I was standing before him. Until that moment, I hadn't even considered the possibility that he and the other leaders might be planning to stone me!

"Nicanor," I began, "I do not deserve grace or mercy or forgiveness from you or any of your brothers and sisters. I am an undeserving sinner who has done great evil against you and so many others. But by His unexplainable mercy, Jesus has extended forgiveness to me and saved me from my sin. He has made me a new creation and I stand before you clothed in His righteousness. I stand before you, seeking your forgiveness. Jesus has called me to serve Him, but I know I cannot serve Him if I have not first been reconciled to you and my other brothers and sisters in Christ. I completely understand if you cannot forgive me and accept me. It would be within your right to take my life for what I have done. I stand before you to do with me as you will."

The two of us looked at one another in silence. I had no idea what he would do or say, but I trusted Jesus. If they were to stone me, I would be with Him in paradise this very day!

"Saul," Nicanor began slowly, "Jesus has not only spoken to you and then to Ananias through visions, He has also come to me. He said, 'Do not be afraid. I have chosen Saul to be My instrument to take My message to the Gentiles, as well as to the people of Israel. Receive him as your brother. Do not punish him, for I will show him how much he must suffer for Me. Forgive him, as I have forgiven you. Receive him, as I have received you. Give to him, as I have given you.'

"So Saul, I can do no less than what my Lord has told me to do." With that, he walked toward me and embraced me. Two men who had seen each other as enemies were now embracing as brothers. Tears began to flow from both our hearts. I had already known that Jesus had forgiven me for all I had done, but it was at that moment I felt His forgiveness. I felt the burden lifted off me. I knew I had been cleansed ... but now I felt clean.

Nicanor and Ananias took me into the city so we could have a meal together. He took me to an upper room of a home that abutted the city wall. As we entered, I saw a group of men and women also gathered there. They appeared to be expecting me. Nicanor began introducing me to each one. These were the other leaders and some of the other believers in the city. Each one greeted me and embraced me as a brother. I have never before – or since – been greeted so warmly. I immediately felt at home with these men and women.

Throughout the night, they shared their testimonies of how they had come to believe in Jesus, and I shared mine with them. No one, except me, made any mention of my past. It was as if everything I had ever done to persecute them had been forgotten. It truly was … amazing grace!

The next morning, I went with Nicanor, Ananias, and Judas to the synagogue. Several of the leaders there knew who I was and why I had come to Damascus. They were surprised when they saw me with Nicanor and Ananias. They knew them to be followers of Jesus. The puzzled look on their faces told me what they were thinking: had I somehow deceived Nicanor and Ananias and was preparing to arrest them?

As was their practice since I was a visitor, they invited me to speak to the men gathered. Someone had just read from the writings of the prophet Isaiah:

He was despised and rejected – a Man of sorrows, acquainted with deepest grief. We turned our backs on Him and looked the other way. He was despised, and we did not care. Yet it was our weaknesses He carried; it was our sorrows that weighed Him down. And we thought His troubles were a punishment from God, a punishment for His own sins! But He was pierced for our rebellion, crushed for our sins. He was beaten so we could be whole. He was whipped so we could be healed. All of us, like sheep, have strayed away. We have left God's paths to follow our own. Yet the Lord laid on Him the sins of us all.[2]

I stood and said, "Brothers, you know why I have come to your city. *I have always lived before God with a clear conscience.*[3] As many of you *are well aware, I was given a thorough Jewish training from my earliest childhood* in Tarsus and in Jerusalem. *I have been a member of the Pharisees, the strictest sect of our religion.*[4] I have done everything I *could to oppose the very name of Jesus the Nazarene.* Indeed, I have done *just that in Jerusalem. Authorized by the leading priests, I caused many believers there to be sent to prison. And I cast my vote against them when they were condemned to death. Many times I had them punished in the synagogues to get them to curse Jesus.* I have been *so violently opposed to them that I even chased them* to your city.[5]

• • •

"Several days ago, as I approached your city *armed with the authority and commission of the leading priests, a light from heaven brighter than the sun shone down on me and my companions. I fell down, and I heard a voice saying to me in Aramaic, 'Saul, Saul, why are you persecuting Me? It is useless for you to fight against My will.'*

"*'Who are you, lord?'* I asked.

"*And the Lord replied, 'I am Jesus, the One you are persecuting. Now get to your feet! For I have appeared to you to appoint you as My servant and witness. Tell the people that you have seen Me and tell them to open their eyes, so they may turn from darkness to light and from the power of Satan to God. Then they will receive forgiveness for their sins and be set apart by faith in Me.'"*[6]

As I spoke, I could sense the power of the Holy Spirit speaking through me. He gave me clarity and boldness. "This same Jesus is the One to whom the prophet Isaiah was referring. He was the Man of sorrows, despised and rejected by us! He was beaten so we could be whole. He was whipped so we could be healed. And He was slain for the sins of us all.

"Turn to the One who truly is the Son of God and receive forgiveness for your sins. Turn from your darkness to His light."

At first, they were all too stunned to speak. Perhaps they thought I was setting a trap for the followers of Jesus who were in their midst. Or perhaps they thought they had misheard me. Gradually, some of the men began to debate with me, but the Holy Spirit gave me the words to rightly respond. No one was able to successfully refute my proofs that Jesus was indeed the Messiah.

Eventually, those who refused to believe left the synagogue, but Ananias, Nicanor, and I continued to speak with those whose hearts were receptive to the truth. Many came to believe in Jesus that day!

. . .

We returned to the synagogue the next two days. Each time, more and more people were there. The new believers were bringing friends to hear from the one who once had persecuted believers but now was a believer himself. By God's grace, many more surrendered their lives and turned to Jesus.

But by the third evening, Ananias, Nicanor, and the other leaders told me I needed to leave the city. Some of the Jewish leaders were plotting to kill me. I retired to my room to pray. That night Jesus came to me in a vision and told me to travel to the wilderness of Arabia. He was calling me to be one of His apostles. The word "apostle" means one who has been with Jesus. The twelve apostles in Jerusalem had walked with Him for over three years, from His baptism by John the baptizer until the day He ascended into heaven.

Jesus was now inviting me to come walk through the wilderness with Him. Little did I know it would be my own three-year journey with Him. He had much to teach me and show me. I wasn't yet ready for the assignment He had for me, but He would get me ready. He would be my Teacher – and I would be His talmid (disciple).

Before the sun rose the next morning, I bid farewell to all of my new brothers in Damascus and set out on my journey.

* * *

7

I received my message from no human source, and no one taught me. Instead, I received it by direct revelation from Jesus Christ.[1]

* * *

When the followers of Jesus scattered from Jerusalem, the Hellenistic believers had quickly migrated to the north and west, making their way to Cilicia, Cappadocia, Pontus, Asia, Phrygia, and Pamphylia. When I was plotting to persecute the believers, I had referred to that group as the western dispersion or the "Cretans." The group that spread among the Parthians, Medes, Elamites, and dwellers of Mesopotamia, I called the eastern dispersion or the "Arabians." Damascus was the northern edge of the region that comprised the Arabian dispersion.

I originally came to this Arabian land to persecute believers who had scattered here to make additional disciples. It was only fitting that Jesus was now going to lead me to follow Him throughout this same region. But that first morning, as I made my way south on the same road where I had first encountered Jesus, He told me to look to the west. Off in the distance I saw the tallest peak on the horizon – Mount Hermon. The mount marked the northern limit of God's promised land to His chosen people.

Our people had always considered it a sacred mountain. The psalmists had extolled its majesty and loftiness in magnifying the works of the Creator. King David himself had written that the dew of Mount Hermon was like a precious blessing from Jehovah God.(2)

I heard the voice of my Teacher directing me to go to the mountain. Without hesitation, I turned off the road and began my four-day journey through the wilderness. As I started to climb Mount Hermon, I found myself walking though snow. It was no wonder the mount was often called the "gray-haired mountain" or the mountain of snow.

The higher I climbed, the snow became deeper, and the temperatures started to plummet. I had not prepared for such weather when I left home, but though my body was cold, my heart was warm. I knew Jesus had led me to this place so that I might hear from Him.

When I reached the summit the next day, I was no longer cold. Before me stood Jesus! Everything about Him was radiant. It wasn't a blinding light like I had experienced on the road outside of Damascus. But it was the most brilliant pure light I had ever seen. I immediately fell to my knees. The words of the prophet Isaiah immediately came to my mind, and I cried out, *"Woe is me! For I am lost; for I am a man of unclean lips, and I dwell in the midst of a people of unclean lips; for my eyes have seen the King, the Lord of hosts!"*(3)

I felt His hand on my shoulder as He said, "Saul, *Don't be afraid! I am the First and the Last. I am the Living One. I died, but look – I am alive forever and ever! And I hold the keys of death and the grave."*(4)

• • •

Slowly, I looked up ... into the eyes of my Lord and Savior. I had heard His voice before, and I had seen Him in visions. But at that moment, I was looking directly into His eyes. He was standing before me. I was kneeling in His presence. He reached down and took me by the hand and lifted me to my feet.

"Saul," He said, "I have chosen you to be My instrument *to take My message to the Gentiles, and to kings, as well as the people of Israel.* Arise and walk with Me *and I will show* you *how much* you *must suffer for Me.*(5) I stood on this very mountain with Peter, James, and John. They marveled when Elijah and Moses appeared and began talking with Me. They heard the Father call out to them, *'This is My dearly loved Son. Listen to Him.'*(6) Just as I taught them, I will teach you. Just as they walked with me, you will walk with me. Just as they will suffer for My sake, you will suffer for My sake."

For the next three days, He patiently taught me and answered my questions. I cannot begin to tell you everything He said or everything I asked. I felt like I learned more truth in those three days than I had in five years at the feet of Gamaliel. I do not say that to belittle Rabbi Gamaliel. I simply say it to tell you that as I listened to Jesus, I drank from a fountain of living water that can never run dry.

I neither ate nor drank during those days. His words were my food. His very presence quenched my thirst. I did not sleep, and I did not grow tired, because His very Spirit gave me rest and strength. It was as if time stood still. And though I didn't want the time to end, I knew it must. I knew He had chosen me for His purpose, and He would lead me to be about the work for which He had called me. Though He did not physically walk down the mountain with me at the end of those three days, He was with me, nonetheless. And He has walked with me every day since!

Jesus continued to teach me as I journeyed the next two days to Hippos, the northernmost city of the Decapolis. The Decapolis is a group of ten cities located on the most eastern frontier of the Roman Empire, east of the

Jordan River. Each of the ten cities has been granted a certain degree of autonomy by the Romans. Each is responsible for its own local rule and mints its own coinage. The presence of Roman soldiers is much less pervasive than the occupied provinces of Judea, Samaria, and Galilee. But as frontier cities, they lack many of the amenities and benefits of a free city like Tarsus.

Hippos was built on a flat-topped foothill that overlooks the Sea of Galilee from its eastern shore. It is directly across the sea from the Galilean capital city of Tiberias. Though both cities enjoy the presence of great ports to facilitate trade, there is hostility between them that developed during the reign of Herod the Great. Since Hippos was primarily inhabited by Gentiles, Herod had treated the people of the city with disdain. So, even though Herodian rule over Hippos had ceased with his death, the contempt remained. Nonetheless, there is still a small Jewish population in the city.

I searched for the local synagogue when I arrived. Though I knew Jesus had chosen me to deliver His message of salvation to the Gentiles, I wanted to first make that message known to God's chosen people.

Soon after I introduced myself in the synagogue, one of the leaders told me he had heard of my efforts to persecute the followers of Jesus while I was in Jerusalem. He invited me to share greetings from the temple in Jerusalem.

In response, I began, "Brothers – you sons of Abraham, and those of you who are God-fearing Gentiles – the message of salvation has been sent to us! The people in Jerusalem and their leaders did not recognize Jesus as the One the prophets had spoken about. Instead, they condemned Him, and in doing this they fulfilled the words of the psalmist, *'The stone that the builders rejected has now become the cornerstone.'*[7] They found no legal reason to execute Him, but they asked Pilate to have Him killed anyway.

. . .

"When they had done all the prophecies said about Him, they took Him down from the cross and placed Him in a tomb. But God raised Him from the dead! And over a period of many days, He appeared to those who had gone with Him from Galilee to Jerusalem. They are now His witnesses to the people of Israel.

"And now I am here to bring you this Good News. The promise that was made to our ancestors has been fulfilled by God for us, their descendants, by raising His Son, Jesus. Through Him there is forgiveness for your sins. Everyone who believes in Him is made right in God's sight – something the law of Moses could never do. Be careful! Do not reject Him as our leaders did in Jerusalem. Don't let the psalmist's words apply to you as well."

The men asked me how one who once persecuted those who followed Jesus was now proclaiming His message of salvation. I told them of my experience on the road to Damascus as well as all He had shown me since. I told them I had been blind – in more ways than one – but now He had allowed me to see.

Afterward, a few of the men came to me, including one named Enos. He told me he had been a criminal and a robber who had become possessed by the demons of Orcus. He had been enticed by their promises of wealth and enslaved by their controlling presence in his life.

Eventually, the officials of his home city of Gerasa had banished him to the wilderness outside of town, not far from Hippos. For years he had endured torment in the tombs of that uninhabited wilderness along the shore. One day, a Man had arrived on a boat. He commanded the demons to come out of Enos. They had begged Him not to send them to some distant place. So, He sent them into a large herd of pigs. The entire herd had plunged into a lake and drowned.

. . .

"I begged Jesus to allow me to go with Him," Enos said. "But He told me to remain here, to tell my family what He had done, and how merciful He had been to me. That was seven years ago. For two years, I traveled throughout Decapolis telling others about Him and the miracle He had performed in my life.

"Then I heard He had been crucified. I could not imagine what He had done or why the religious leaders in Jerusalem would have Him executed. I lived in despair for years. But today, you have given me good news! Jesus is alive! My hope has been restored. He is not only a miracle worker – He truly is the Son of God. He is not a man whom others could destroy."

Then Enos exclaimed, "Jesus, forgive me for my doubts. I will never doubt You again!"

I remained in Hippos for several more days teaching in the synagogue. Enos remained by my side. Soon, however, the leaders of the synagogue came and told me I was not welcome – they would no longer permit me to disrupt their teaching. Like too many of our religious leaders, they also were rejecting the counsel of God.(8)

Before I left the synagogue, Jesus gave me these words for them: *"It was necessary that I first preach the word of God to you Jews. But since you have rejected it and judged yourselves unworthy of eternal life, I will offer it to the Gentiles. For the Lord gave me this command when He said, 'I have made you a light to the Gentiles, to bring salvation to the farthest corners of the earth.'"*(9)

It was then the Lord showed me I should follow that practice in every city I entered. I was first to go to the local synagogue, and if and when the local Jews rejected the counsel of God, I was to go to the Gentiles.

As Enos and I stood before the Gentiles in Hippos that day, I proclaimed the message of salvation. Many Gentiles received the message that day and more in the days that followed. Those believers began to spread the Lord's message throughout the nearby cities of Philoterio, Gadara, and Abila.

After a few weeks passed, Enos asked if I would travel to his hometown of Gerasa to share about Jesus. He explained that his family and others he had told about Jesus had lost hope when they heard of His crucifixion. We most definitely had good news for them!

It was a five-day journey to Gerasa. The time together gave me opportunity to teach Enos about what the prophets had written about Jesus. I realized he had little knowledge of the Scriptures, and I knew he was part of the reason Jesus had brought me to this place. Jesus had made an overnight trip across the sea just to deliver Enos and save him seven years earlier, knowing that He would later send me to disciple him. It reminded me of how God orders our steps and directs our paths. And I was certain this would not be the last time.

When we arrived in Gerasa, Enos led us to the home of his elderly parents. I watched their demeanor completely transform as Enos shared that Jesus is alive. When Enos told them about my encounters with Jesus, they turned and looked at me for affirmation. Within minutes they were calling for their neighbors and friends to come hear. Quite a celebration erupted as the news made its way through the group that Jesus truly is the Son of God.

I knew Enos was quite capable of answering their many questions, so I excused myself and made my way to the synagogue. By the time I got there, news of our arrival and the resulting commotion at Enos's parents' home had already circulated.

As I entered the synagogue, the man who evidently was spreading the news turned and pointed me out to the men with whom he was speaking. "Surely this can't be true," the chief rabbi said to me. "Who are you and why do you bring such outrageous news?"

"My name is Saul," I began. "*I am a Jew born in Tarsus, a city in Cilicia, and I was educated in Jerusalem under Gamaliel. As his student, I was carefully trained in our Jewish laws and customs. I became very zealous to honor God in everything I did, just like all of you today. And I persecuted the followers of the Way, hounding some to death, arresting both men and women and throwing them in prison. The high priest and the whole council of elders can testify that this is so. For I received letters from them to our Jewish brothers in Damascus, authorizing me to bring the followers of the Way from there to Jerusalem, in chains, to be punished.*"

I concluded my account of my encounter with Jesus on the road to Damascus by saying, "*I was blinded by the intense light and had to be led by the hand to Damascus by my companions. A man named Ananias lived there. He was a godly man, deeply devoted to the law, and well regarded by all the Jews of Damascus. He came and stood beside me and said, 'Brother Saul, regain your sight.' And that very moment I could see him!*

"*Then he told me, 'The God of our ancestors has chosen you to know His will and to see the Righteous One and hear Him speak. For you are to be His witness, telling everyone what you have seen and heard.'*"[10]

I continued, "I stand before you as a witness to the One I have seen with my own eyes, who has mercifully forgiven me of my sins, and who has cleansed me of my unrighteousness. I am one who was blind, but now I see. And the Righteous One has sent me to bring you this same message of Good News!"

Some of the men believed and were saved. Each morning afterward, I returned to the synagogue to teach a growing crowd of people who gathered. In the late afternoons, I would sit with Enos outside the doorway of his parents' home and teach an increasing number of Gentiles who were assembling to hear the truth about Jesus.

* * *

8

Now teach these truths to other trustworthy people who will be able to pass them on to others.[1]

* * *

On the fifteenth morning after our arrival in Gerasa, I went to the synagogue as usual to teach. The chief rabbi immediately confronted me. "The day after you first arrived, we sent a reliable messenger to the temple in Jerusalem to confirm you are who you say you are. He has now returned to us with this message from the high priest.

"The message reads: 'It is true we sent Saul of Tarsus to Damascus, authorizing him to bring followers of The Way from there to Jerusalem, in chains, to be punished for their rebellion and blasphemy. But somewhere along the way he became mad. The men we sent with him returned and reported that he suffered heatstroke and was blinded by the sun. In his delirium, he began to rant that he had seen the blasphemer whom we had crucified. He claimed the blasphemer was alive – but we know Him to be dead. Do not be deceived by the rantings of this mad man. He has become a blasphemer himself and only seeks to deceive you!'"

. . .

Then the chief rabbi commanded the men with him to take me before the city council. "This man must be punished," he said. "He is disturbing the citizens of our city with his false teachings. He is professing that our allegiance should be to another king – a dead king – One whose name was Jesus. He too was crucified for His rebellion and false teachings. This man deserves the same fate!"

There were no Roman leaders living in Gerasa since it was a frontier city. The only Roman presence was a small garrison of soldiers, most of whom had been enlisted locally. The city council was free to make its own decision in any matter with one exception – they were not permitted to mete out capital punishment.

I was grateful no charges were made against Enos. I explained to the council what I had said and my circumstances and experiences leading up to this false accusation. My explanation, however, seemed to fall on deaf ears. I then told them I was a Roman citizen who deserved a fair trial before Roman authorities before any judgment could be administered. But the council had no interest in referring the matter to Roman authorities. They were empowered to dispense any justice needed, up to the maximum permitted under Roman rule. They decided I would receive a scourging of forty lashes minus one. Forty lashes was considered a death sentence, but thirty-nine was within the authority of the city council.

I realized the soldiers were savoring the moment as they took me away to receive my punishment. Roman soldiers were not liked or respected by the citizens of the frontier; in fact, most people resented them. So, they took no pity on their victims; rather, they relished those rare times when they were permitted to release their pent-up frustrations.

They stripped me of my cloak and then two soldiers flogged me with their lead-tipped whips. They patiently – yet viciously – struck me one after the other, starting at the top of my back and proceeding down to my ankles, then moving back up my body. I knew my Lord had been without fault when He was scourged in the same way. However, I had persecuted His followers. I was deserving of this treatment – not for that of which I was accused – but so much more.

I knew Jesus was right there with me through every blow. He gave me the grace and the strength to endure the pain. Though I knew this punishment would not lead to death, my mind recalled the expression on Stephen's face the day he was stoned to death. His face had reflected a peace I could not understand at the time. But now I did as I looked into the face of Jesus in the midst of the viciousness being unleashed on me.

The soldiers untied me when they finished, and I fell to the ground. Enos and another believer picked me up and carried me away. They bathed my wounds and treated them. I remained in Enos's home for several weeks to heal and recover. My bed became my lectern as I taught Enos and others that God was raising up leaders from the new host of believers in Gerasa.

Once I had fully recuperated, I knew it was time to go. Enos and the others would continue the work God had begun here. Rather than being frightened by the punishment I received, they were courageous as the Spirit of God empowered them as His witnesses. The flame of the Gospel would burn brightly in Gerasa and would spread. Jesus showed me my work here was finished.

He led me on a three-day journey to the most southern city of the Decapolis – Philadelphia. The city was primarily inhabited by Greek Gentiles. I already knew these Gentiles resented the Jewish leaders in Judea. Their resentment dated back to the rule of the Jewish Hasmonean kings, who had treated the Gentiles with much disrespect. The Gentiles, for their part, saw the Hasmoneans as a narrow-minded and unenlightened people. Neither group had much tolerance for the other's religious practice.

The Roman occupation, though seen as oppressive by the Jews, was greeted as liberating by the Gentiles. Many of them had migrated from the

Iudaean province to the cities of the Decapolis to escape the discrimination they still felt. They now enjoyed the protection and sophistication of the Roman way of life. They were more than willing to help protect this frontier land on behalf of Rome to be out from underneath the bondage of the Jews.

Most of the cities also included a smaller population of Jews. Their presence dated back to the days following the Babylonian captivity. These families had chosen to remain in the Arabian lands. Under Roman rule, the two groups had learned to inhabit the cities separated from one another – while remaining somewhat tolerant of each other.

Philadelphia was no exception. It had a small Jewish population that gathered in a correspondingly small synagogue. As was my habit, I went to the synagogue to teach soon after I arrived in the city.

On my second day, I was approached by a man as we were both leaving the synagogue. He told me his name was Malchus and said he had heard me speak about Jesus. "I met Jesus once," he began. "At the time, I was a servant to the high priest Caiaphas. He had sent me under the cover of darkness with a group of servants and guards to arrest Jesus.

"We had no idea how His followers would react. When we came upon them, all of them were sleeping except Jesus. As we approached Him, the rest of the men began to stir. One of the men – a little older, a little bigger, and a little burlier than the rest – drew his sword. I raised my club to knock the sword out of his hand. But the man was quicker than I was, and I felt his blade slice off my ear.

"I instinctively dropped my club and clutched at the right side of my head. I could feel that my ear was no longer there. As the blood poured down my neck from my open wound, my knees buckled, and I dropped to the ground. I looked down and saw that my cloak was already covered in blood. My head started to spin, and I knew at any moment I was going to black out.

"I heard someone shout, '*No more of this! Put away your sword. Don't you realize that I could ask My Father for thousands of angels to protect us, and He would send them instantly?*'[11]

"Suddenly, I sensed Someone was kneeling in front of me. It was Jesus! And He had placed His hand on the side of my face. Instantly the pain stopped! I tried to understand what He was doing. When He took His hand away, I immediately raised mine. As my hand touched the side of my head, I realized my ear was there – right where it was supposed to be! My ear, that moments ago had been separated from my head, was now back in its place. I was no longer bleeding! Had I imagined my ear being cut off? When I looked down again, I saw my cloak soaked in blood. No, I had not imagined it!

"Jesus was still there kneeling before me. I looked into His eyes. There I was on a mission to arrest Him. But He wasn't looking at me with hatred or contempt – all I saw in His eyes was gentleness and kindness. The Man whom I had come to arrest had shown me mercy. He had shown me compassion. He had healed my pain. I mouthed the words, 'Thank You.' But they were so inadequate. I began to tremble before Him.

"It all lasted only seconds, but it left an indelible print on my heart and in my mind. As I looked at the faces of those around me, they also were looking on in disbelief. But then I saw the captain of the guard reach down, take Jesus by the hand, and jerk Him to His feet. As I knelt there, they tied ropes around His wrists. The man who had cut off my ear with his sword, and all the rest of Jesus's followers, had scattered and run away.

"The captain of the guard commanded the soldiers and servants to take Jesus and go. Soon, I was left there by myself. The chaos had vanished, and I was kneeling in silence. I realized my life had been forever changed by His simple touch. I now had a new Master. I was no longer the servant of the high priest; I was now a servant of Jesus.

"For the next few days, I kept hidden in Jerusalem. My heart ached as I witnessed the crucifixion of Jesus – I couldn't believe He was dead. I felt responsible. I had been a part of the group that had arrested Him. But three days later, I heard reports that He had risen from the grave. He was alive!

"I didn't know what to do. I was a runaway servant, and I knew I couldn't stay in Jerusalem. Caiaphas had people looking for me. He was accusing me of having turned his own daughter against him when she boldly announced her belief in Jesus. Jerusalem had always been my home. I didn't know where to go. But I began to sense I was supposed to come east to the frontier – and specifically here to Philadelphia – the 'city of brotherly love.' Caiaphas would not search for me here. I would be safe.

"For six years I have been hiding in Philadelphia. But today, when I heard you, I knew I could not continue to hide any longer. I know Jesus is the Son of God. He healed me. He forgave me. He has given me a new purpose. And I believe He has brought you here to show me what I must do."

Jesus had now led me to another man I was to disciple and train up to be a co-laborer in the work, just like Enos. The Lord had shown me I would never be able to make His name known to every Gentile, but He would lead me to trustworthy people who would teach others. Malchus would not be my first, and he most certainly would not be my last!

I returned to the synagogue several more times, trying to convince the Jews the Messiah they were looking for had already come. I walked them through the Scriptures, but it was to no avail. The Jews opposed me and rejected the truth about Jesus. They insulted me to the point the Lord had me shake the dust from my robe and say, *"Your blood is upon your own heads. I am innocent. I will preach to the Gentiles."*(3)

For the next year and a half, I made a living working among the Gentiles with Enos by my side. The people became more receptive when they learned the leaders of the synagogue rejected me and that I was from Tarsus. I was able to acquire a booth in the marketplace, and soon I was mending tents. As I worked, I would tell those around me about Jesus. As the weeks and months passed, many surrendered their lives to Christ.

The new believers began to gather each night in the home of Malchus. At first, I taught the group; but as time passed, Malchus began to do more and more of the teaching. After a year, several of the new believers were now teaching as well. The size of the group soon exceeded what Malchus's home could accommodate. Believers were now gathering in multiple homes around the city.

During my time in Philadelphia, I became acutely aware that my eyesight was diminishing. More and more I needed to shield my eyes from the sunlight to see objects clearly. Soon I was squinting so I could distinguish the faces of those I was approaching. I had always prided myself on my excellent vision, but now I needed to rely on Malchus and others to help me see.

However, Jesus continued to lead me to spend time alone with Him in the wilderness outside Philadelphia for days at a time. On those days, He was my eyes. My failing eyesight not only demanded I depend on Him for His direction as I walked with Him, it also kept distractions from my view. Jesus used those times to teach me to trust Him completely.

He told me He had taught Simon Peter to walk on the strength of His Word in the middle of the Sea of Galilee. Now He was teaching me to "step out of the boat" and walk on the sureness of His Word in the wilderness. He told me that just as Peter had begun to sink in the waves when he took his eyes off Jesus, I would also sink if I did the same.

I had always been a self-reliant man, depending on my own knowledge and wisdom for answers. I relied on my own strength to accomplish that which was before me to do. I relied on my business acumen to provide for my needs. I relied on my own capabilities to accomplish any task placed before me. But Jesus was teaching me it was through my weakness that His power works through me. He repeatedly taught me in word and in deed His grace was always sufficient. He was teaching me to trust Him completely. I knew that was a lesson He would continue to teach me.

I first experienced my Lord's healing touch working through me in Philadelphia. We were gathered in Malchus's home. Two men who had recently surrendered their lives to Jesus had brought their lame friend to our gathering. They told us their friend had been lame since birth – but they had heard Jesus made the lame to walk. They asked if Jesus could heal their friend.

The room was silent as everyone waited for the answer. I knew Jesus had healed many people throughout His ministry. I knew God had healed others through the spoken word of Simon Peter and the other apostles. But He had never done so through me. It was a deciding moment in my life. Was I willing by faith to allow His power to work through my weakness? Did I believe He was still able to heal? And specifically, did I believe He could heal this man?

I knew Jesus was waiting for me to answer. Was I willing to allow Him to do immeasurably more than I could ask or imagine, according to His power at work within me? I turned to the man and asked, "Do you believe Jesus is able to heal you?"

The lame man answered, "I do!"

. . .

"Then stand up!" I replied. Without any hesitation, he took my hand and stood to his feet. He took a step and then another. Within moments, he was walking. We all began to praise God. The man turned and thanked me, but I told him to direct his thanks to the One who had made Him walk – the Lord Jesus Christ!

I knew Jesus had just invited me to step out of the boat – and I wasn't supposed to get back in it. He was commanding me to "walk on the water" – and I knew He would never let me sink.

* * *

9

The governor under King Aretas kept guards at the city gates to catch me.[1]

* * *

My work in the Decapolis was finished, and it was time to continue my journey through the Arabian wilderness. Enos and Malchus, together with many other believers, would continue the work in Philadelphia. Jesus was leading me to go with Him farther south into the Nabatean Kingdom to the city of Petra.

Malchus accompanied me on the two-week journey. We set out in the month of Tishri, two weeks after the beginning of the new year. We traveled along the King's Highway, the trade route connecting Africa and Egypt with Mesopotamia. The Nabateans had a reputation for being masterful traders. They primarily traded in frankincense and myrrh harvested from the trees that grew throughout their land, bitumen mined from the bottom of the Dead Sea, and spices unique to their region.

The Nabateans had coexisted in these lands with the Jews for over 500 years, dating back to the days of the Babylonian captivity. But when the

Hasmoneans ruled Judea, they attempted to forcefully convert the Nabateans to Judaism. The Nabateans rebelled and remained at war with the Jews. Their current king, Aretas, had come into power during that conflict, some forty-five years prior to my journey to Petra.

Many years ago, King Aretas and Herod the Great entered into a treaty with one another attempting to end the conflict. To seal their agreement, Aretas's daughter, Phasaelis, was given in marriage to Herod's son, Antipas. However, after Herod's death, Antipas divorced Phasaelis so he could marry his stepbrother's daughter, Herodias. Public opposition to that adulterous and incestuous marriage was what led to the beheading of John the baptizer, the prophet who had heralded the arrival of Jesus.

King Aretas wasted no time seeking revenge for the offense to Phasaelis – and to himself. Even though both territories were now under Roman rule, he invaded the domain of Herod Antipas and resoundingly defeated the Herodian army. Antipas only survived the invasion because of the Roman forces' help. King Aretas would have been content to leave the matter there, but Antipas appealed to Emperor Tiberius for retribution.

The emperor agreed and dispatched the governor of Syria, Lucius Vitellius the Elder, to attack Aretas, which escalated the conflict. Aretas was furious and led his forces to thoroughly defeat the Syrian army. On the eve of Aretas's victory, many kilometers away in the city of Rome, Emperor Tiberius died. His successor, Caligula, had no interest in furthering the conflict, so Aretas was left with the spoils of his victory. He was now the ruler over the Syrian and Nabatean kingdoms. Without further action, the conflict between Aretas and Antipas subsided, the former returning to his home in Petra and the latter to Tiberias.

Few places rival the aura and grandeur of Petra. The city is carved out of a soft red sandstone, giving it the descriptive name, "Rose City." My two-week journey with Malchus along the King's Highway concluded with a thirty-minute walk through the most majestic entry into a city I have ever seen. The entry is a towering slot canyon called the Siq. It starts out as a wide gravel path, but quickly the canyon walls burst forth toward the sky almost 180 meters, completely enveloping the pathway that narrows to three meters in several places.

Suddenly the canyon opened into the city. Our first sight was that of an elaborate edifice being carved into the sandstone. Even with my diminishing eyesight, I could see it was a remarkable display of Nabataean craftsmanship. We soon learned it was a tomb being built for King Aretas.

As we continued, we passed other tombs that held the remains of previous kings, as well as many temples. We noticed the Nabateans were pantheistic – likenesses of their many gods were prominently displayed everywhere. The most visible was the god Dushara, whom they referred to as their god over all gods. His likeness was that of a man holding the light of the sun in one hand and a shepherd's staff in the other. I was gripped by the lostness of the people of Petra and their great need to hear the Good News of Jesus.

We began looking for a place to stay for the night. Malchus introduced us, explaining that he was from Philadelphia, and I was from Tarsus. We didn't realize just how providential that introduction was; it didn't take long for us to realize Jews were not welcome in Petra. The memories of forced conversions still lingered in the minds of their oldest citizens, and the more recent armed conflict between King Aretas and Antipas had caused a deep-seated hatred for Jews. It was obvious there was no synagogue in Petra. So, I chose to seek out teachers and scholars in the city. I was told about a Parthian scholar who was widely respected for his great knowledge about many things.

The next morning Malchus and I were told where we could find this scholar, whose name was Yanzu. He was about twenty years older than I was. He told us he was from Babylon and had been the servant and student of one of the leading Parthian magi named Balthazar. Upon his master's death, he had been granted his freedom from servitude. He had set out on a journey through the Nabatean Kingdom headed to

Jerusalem. But he had stopped here in Petra over ten years ago and had never left.

I asked him why he had headed to Jerusalem and what made him stay in Petra, but I never anticipated the story he told us.

"When I was a boy," he began, "my master took me with him on an expedition to follow a star in search of a king. He charged me with the safekeeping of the gift he intended to present to the king. We all expected the star would lead us to a great palace, but instead it led us to a simple home in the town of Bethlehem. When I brought the gift into the home, I followed my master to a small room.

"I never imagined I would be granted permission to come before this great king, but when I arrived at the door my master motioned for me to join him in the room. I was being allowed to enter the King's presence! I don't have the words to tell you how I felt. After I handed the gift to my master, I fell on my knees and kept my eyes lowered. I knew I was in the presence of One who deserved great honor.

"My master also knelt as he gave his gift to the baby's mother. As she opened the chest, the sweet smell of frankincense filled the air. The smell caused me to look up. The mother and baby were both dressed plainly – not in the fine clothing I had expected. But as I looked into the baby's eyes, I knew His were the eyes of a King! And not just any king!

"I looked at my master as he, too, knelt before the baby. And I realized he and I were the same before this baby. This little One was the King before whom every knee must bow. I knew He was my King – just as much as He was my master's King. And I knew I would always be welcome in His presence.

. . .

"As we left that night, I asked my master the King's name. He told me, 'His name is Jesus. And He is not just any king, but the King of all kings. The star has led us to Him. Though we must leave Him now, we must keep Him in our hearts wherever we go.'

"That was the only time I saw this King. That was over forty years ago. Ten years ago, when my master died, he granted me my freedom on his deathbed. I decided right then to set out to find the King again. I traveled through this city because we had stopped here years before on our return home to Babylon. I only intended to stay here a couple of days, but on my second night I received a vision. In it, I was told to wait here in this city for a man who would come tell me what has happened to the King. I have been waiting ever since."

Yanzu also told us how his master had stopped at Herod's palace in Jerusalem on their way to find the baby. Herod had instructed them to bring him word of the baby's location after they found him. But his master had been warned in a dream not to return to Herod. So instead of returning home by way of Jerusalem, they had proceeded south around the lower tip of the Dead Sea – then on to this city before traveling home.

I then began to tell him about Jesus. I shared with him about the miracles He had performed and the truth He had taught. Malchus told his story of how he had been one of the men who arrested Jesus. Yanzu was horrified. When I told him about Jesus's crucifixion, Yanzu was inconsolable. "How could you arrest the King?" he asked as he looked at Malchus. "And how could they crucify Him?" he cried out between sobs.

But I quickly regained his attention as I announced Jesus was alive! He had risen from the dead three days later. Yanzu was beside himself. He was living out these events as he heard them. In a matter of moments, he had traveled the full spectrum of emotions.

. . .

At that point, I told him the words of the prophets dating back to Abraham. He was familiar with many of them. His master had taught him well. But others he had not yet heard. They all now began to make sense to him.

He asked me where Jesus was now. I said He had returned to heaven to prepare a place for us. But then I told him how Jesus had come to me on the road to Damascus, and how He was leading me in this journey through the Arabian wilderness. "Yanzu, He is leading you as well. He led you to this place. He led Malchus and me to find you and you to find us – so we could hear your story and you could hear ours. The King you sought as a child now reigns on His throne. Now that you have found Him, you must lead others to Him. The whole world needs to hear … and you are one of His witnesses."

Yanzu began to weep again. But this time they were tears of joy. "He has been in my heart since the day I met Him," Yanzu said. "I can do nothing less than tell others about Him!"

Later that night I told Malchus, "The Lord has shown me I must remain here in Petra with Yanzu, but you must return to Gerasa and continue in the work there." The next morning Malchus set out on his journey, and Yanzu and I made our way to the lecture hall in the city.

When we arrived, there was a blind man sitting by the entrance. He asked us for money as we walked by. I sensed the Lord leading me to take him by the hand. As I reached down, I said, "I do not have any money for you. But I will give what I have. What is your name?"

"My name is Obodas," he replied.

"Obodas," I said, "in the name of the Lord Jesus, open your eyes and see!"

• • •

Instantly Obodas could see. I took him by the hand and helped him up. He raised his other hand over his eyes to shield them from the bright light. He rapidly blinked his eyes. "What have you done?" he asked. "What is happening to me?" In a few minutes, his eyes began to adjust, and he looked at me. He took hold of my hands and stared into my eyes. "I can see you!" he said. "I can see!"

He turned his head and looked around him. "I see the sky! I see the people! I see my own hands!" He began to move around. He walked right up to other people who were gathered there and stared at them saying, "I can see you!"

Several men who had been watching walked over. "Obodas has been blind since birth," one of the men said. "He has sat in front of this hall for years. What has happened to him? Are you a god?"

The men began to shout to others there. "This man here with Yanzu is a god in human form!"

"No, my friends," I shouted. "I am no god! I am a human being just like you. But I have come to tell you about the one true God – the One who has created all things, the One who has given sight to Obodas, and the One who has made the way for all of us to see Him and know Him!"

The crowd around us grew as more people realized what had happened. "God is not a man, and He is not made of stone," I said. "Neither is He made by human hands. He is alive. Allow me to tell you about Him." For the next several hours, I did just that as I shared the Good News. When the day was done, some had believed while others still had questions. I told them I would return the next day.

The next morning the crowd was even larger. Some of the people had brought friends and family members who were sick, lame, or deaf. By

God's grace, He healed each one. Each healing was a testimony of His mercy and His glory. More people believed that day and each day thereafter.

One week later at midday, a group of soldiers showed up at the hall and interrupted as I was speaking. The officer in charge said, "Paul of Tarsus, you are under arrest. You are a Jew attempting to convert our people to Judaism. The whole city is in an uproar because of what you have done. By order of King Aretas, you are to be flogged and thrown into prison."

As they led me away, I was grateful they had not arrested Yanzu. He would be free to continue discipling these new believers. My arrest appeared to be more about the animosity the king held toward Jews than it was about my preaching about Jesus.

God again gave me the grace and strength to endure the scourging I received. But this time, there was no one to attend to my wounds. I was thrown into a dark cell and left to care for myself.

After about a week, I was surprised when Yanzu and Obodas visited. Apparently, they had been petitioning the king on my behalf since the day of my arrest. Yanzu's good reputation obviously placed him in favored status before the king. Though the king was unswerving with regard to my guilt as a Jew, he appeared to hold no grievance toward Yanzu. And the king could not refute that Obodas had been given sight. But he was telling everyone it was a benevolent gesture from the god Dushara. Obodas knew better than that – and so did many others!

But I was grateful God had orchestrated things so my friends could visit me and tend to my needs. While they continued to plead for my release before the king, my body continued to strengthen and recover. During each of their visits, they reported how God was continuing to work in the hearts of the people and how the number of believers was increasing every day.

. . .

I remained in prison for six months. Jesus graciously used each day to draw me closer to Him and teach me more about Himself. He also enabled each of my visits from Yanzu and Obodas to be another opportunity for me to teach them further and equip them for the work God was clearly putting before them. I could see His hand directing every detail.

The day finally came when King Aretas agreed to release me. I was never to return to Petra or any part of the Nabatean or Syrian kingdoms. If I did, I would be executed. I was grateful to have one last visit to encourage Yanzu and Obodas before my departure. The guards arrived while we were still talking and abruptly led me out of the prison and out of the city – all the way through the Siq.

After exiting the canyon, the guards stood watching me as I continued my journey south. God meant for me to walk this part of my journey alone with Jesus. Together, He was leading me to a special place – a place where I was to enter into His presence in a unique way. He was leading me to Mount Sinai.

* * *

10

I had to be lowered in a basket through a window in the city wall to escape.[(1)]

* * *

It took me eighteen days to reach Mount Sinai. Each day the Lord sent ravens in the morning and evening to supply me with bread and meat. He gave me rest each night and strength that was sufficient. He led me by a pool each morning where I could collect enough water for the day's journey. As I traveled, I was acutely aware of how my Lord was going before me just as He had gone before His people when He led them to this very same place. My part in the journey was simply to trust Him and follow Him.

I have traveled many kilometers and many days since then, and I know He has been with me every step of the way. I felt as if I were completely enveloped in His presence – just as if He were going before me to lead me as a pillar of cloud and coming behind me to be my rear guard as a pillar of fire.

. . .

Chapter 10

When I reached the mount, He reminded me this was the
spoken to Moses from the burning bush. It was here He ha
the assignment of leading His people out of slavery. It wa
shared the meal with Moses and seventy-three Israelite le
His covenant with His people. It was here He had invited M
with Him for forty days and forty nights to receive His law for His people. And it was here He had permitted Moses to see Him as He passed by and witness His glorious presence.

For the next forty days and nights I remained on the mount in the presence of my Savior; I did not eat or drink. He alone was my nourishment. He permitted me to behold His glory as He patiently taught me.

Rabbi Gamaliel had taught me there were five epochs of human history since the days of creation. The first was innocence. It had lasted until Adam and Eve fell in their sin and ushered in the second epoch, which was conscience. It had lasted about 1,600 years until God could tolerate sin no more and destroyed all but a remnant in the flood.

The third was the epoch of civil authority constituted by God to govern the society that arose after the flood. But man again rebelled, and God dispersed the people after their attempt to build the Tower of Babel. That ushered in the fourth epoch, which was promise. God created a nation through Abraham and his descendants that would bring glory to His name. He delivered His people from slavery just as He had promised – and He brought them to this very mountain. It was here the fifth epoch had begun – the dispensation of the law He had given to His people.

No matter how hard we tried, our people could not obey His law. We always fell short. We always sinned. We had been so blinded by our sin that we didn't even realize when God fulfilled the law before our very eyes … through Jesus. In our blindness, we had been instruments of His death. But by God's mercy, that had always been His plan – that the blood of Jesus would be shed as the perfect Passover Lamb. And not only would He die, but He would also conquer death and arise from the grave.

• • •

What Rabbi Gamaliel had not taught me was there was a sixth epoch, which began the day Christ rose from the dead. He ushered in the dispensation of grace – unmerited salvation that was extended not only to the people of Israel but to all people. Jesus had brought me to this place to teach me how a people who had not lived under His law would now enter into a relationship with Him under His grace.

In fulfillment of the words given through the prophet Isaiah, Jesus had come to *do more than restore the people of Israel to* the Father. He had *made Him a light to the Gentiles, and to bring salvation to the ends of the earth.*(2)

Jesus had called me and chosen me to be His apostle with the responsibility of building His church among the Gentiles, just as He had given the responsibility to Simon Peter to do the same among the Jews. Just as God had brought Moses to this place to receive the commandments that defined the epoch of law, He had brought me here to receive the truths the Jews and Gentiles needed to live and walk in relationship with God. And Jesus showed me that this epoch will continue until the day He returns – and that could be any day!

Jesus taught me Gentile followers would not need to meet the same requirements expected of His chosen people under the promise and under the law. For instance, the practice of circumcision required for every male Jew would not be required of male Gentile believers.

Also, the strict dietary laws applied to the Jewish people would not be placed on the Gentile believers. Instead, they were to abstain from eating food that had been offered to idols and from consuming blood or eating the meat of strangled animals.

But He also taught me what it would look like for His followers to walk with Him under grace. He had already demonstrated on the Day of Pentecost that His followers would be baptized and indwelt by His Holy Spirit. In that way, each follower would be empowered and equipped for the work of ministry – the work of carrying out Christ's mission and mandate.

He explained that every believer – whether they be Jew or Gentile – is a member of His body, and every member has a different role in the body. Each one is equipped uniquely for that role. He would be most glorified when we come together as the entire body in worship, in witness, and in ministry.

Jesus shared that He would be placing some within the body to be apostles, others to be prophets, and still others to be teachers. Some would perform miracles or gifts of healing, whereas some would have the ability to help or organize. He would give each one different gifts.

In the days that followed, Jesus taught me many things, just as He had His other apostles. I learned that whoever leads in His kingdom must be a servant. Whoever loves his Savior must love his brother and sister. Whoever remains in Him must remain in His Word – knowing that as we remain in His Word, we will know His truth and His truth will empower us.

Jesus shared with me about the night before His crucifixion. He talked about the meal He had with His disciples, what it meant, and His command that His followers observe that supper as we come together in remembrance of Him. He told me to teach the Gentile followers to observe that meal of remembrance.

My days with Him on the mountain passed quickly, but the day arrived when He told me it was time for me to go. It was hard for me to leave and walk down that mountain away from His presence – but I knew His Spirit was going with me. I knew He had not saved me and chosen me to remain on the mountain. He wanted me to be an instrument He could use to accomplish His mission – and the mission wasn't on the mountain, it was in the valley. So off I went in obedience.

The Lord showed me I was to go to the Decapolis city of Pella. Pella was a forty days' journey from Mount Sinai. Though it was a long trip, I knew my Lord would be with me. But what I didn't know was when I got to the bottom of Mount Sinai, the Spirit of the Lord caught me away – and suddenly I was on the outskirts of Pella. What should have taken forty days had been accomplished in the blink of an eye.

In all my travels since then, I have never again experienced anything like that. As a matter of fact, I am only aware of one other person who has. The evangelist Philip once told me the Spirit of the Lord had transported him from the wilderness outside Gaza to the city of Azotus – a three-day journey – all within the blink of an eye. It was another reminder to us both that nothing is impossible for our Lord, and He will do whatever He needs to do to further His mission and His plan.

The city of Pella had been burned to the ground by forces under the command of the Hasmonean king, Alexander Jannaeus, over 100 years before my arrival. He had destroyed the city because its inhabitants had refused to follow Jewish customs. As you can imagine, the destruction of the city created a deep-seated hatred for Jews among the surviving Nabateans who lived in the city. Like most other people living in the Decapolis, their hatred for the Jews was passed from generation to generation as they rebuilt their city.

They did, however, appear to accept Jews who were followers of Jesus. The citizens of Pella had heard that Jesus was considered an enemy by the Jewish religious leaders. The Pellanese knew that Jews had put Him to death. So, they decided any group considered an enemy of the Jews was their friend. That meant when any persecuted followers of The Way scattered from Jerusalem to Pella, they were received with open arms.

. . .

It didn't take me long to learn there was a small group of believers in Pella. And it didn't take them long to realize I was Saul the persecutor. Though I was unaware, a few of them apparently recognized me soon after I arrived. Word went out to the other believers that one of their persecutors had come to take them back to Jerusalem. Soon, some of the Pellanese had also heard the same warning and were appalled. They were certain if one Jew had come, there would soon be more.

I had only been in the city for less than a day when I found myself surrounded by a group of Pellanese men. They shouted their accusations at me but never gave me an opportunity to answer their charges. Before I knew it, I was being pummeled and beaten. Even during the frenzy, I found myself thinking that surely Jesus had not transported me from Mount Sinai to Pella to die at the hands of this crowd. As one fist after another pounded me, I called out to my Lord to save me.

Suddenly, I heard a familiar voice shout, "Stop! This man has not come to persecute anyone. He, too, is a follower of Jesus. Stop beating this man!"

Whoever spoke seemed to be someone of authority because the beating stopped, and the shouts quieted down. I sank to my knees in pain as the crowd backed away. Someone walked through the crowd and approached me. I tried to see who it was, but the sun was shining directly into my eyes. The man knelt in front of me and placed His arm around me. "You are safe now, Saul," he said. "No one will do you any more harm." My comforter's face began to come into focus, and I realized I was looking into the eyes of my friend Malchus.

He embraced me and called out to some of the men to come help him carry me to a place where he could dress my wounds. The men hesitated. I'm not sure if it was out of fear or contempt – or whether they were ashamed about what they had done. But I heard Malchus turn his face heavenward and pray, "Jesus, You once healed me as I also had fallen to my knees. Please heal your servant Saul, and give these men the courage to receive their brother."

. . .

Within moments several men stepped forward to help lift me to my feet. The crowd parted and remained silent as they watched the men carry me away.

By God's mercy, it did not take long for my body to heal. Malchus had brought me to the rooms where he was staying, and he arranged for a physician to treat my injuries. As I recuperated, Malchus explained that he had arrived in Pella about six months earlier. He had returned to Gerasa after we parted ways in Petra. Many men and women had become followers of Jesus. God had raised up leaders from among them to continue the work.

Malchus had heard there was a group of Jewish believers in Pella who needed someone to teach them. He knew the Spirit of the Lord was leading him to come and be that teacher. But since his arrival, he had seen an openness of hearts among the Pellanese Gentiles. There was a growing number who were now becoming followers of Jesus.

"But a disagreement is growing between the Jewish and Gentile believers," he reported. "The Jewish believers are telling the Gentiles they must be circumcised. And there are even disagreements as to what the Gentiles should be permitted to eat. The issue has become even more pronounced when the followers gather for a meal. We don't know what to do. And the question is being asked in many of the other cities throughout the Decapolis as well."

During the weeks that followed, I explained to Malchus and other leaders what Jesus had shown me on Mount Sinai. The Gentile believers readily accepted what I had to say, but the Jewish believers were hesitant. They recognized Gentiles were being given the opportunity by God to become part of His chosen people. There was no question that salvation came through Jesus, but their expression of faith needed to align with the requirements of the law of Moses. I realized these differences needed to be settled quickly, or there would be a deep division within the new and growing church of Jesus Christ.

I knew it was time to go to Jerusalem and speak with the elders of the church. But I also sensed the Spirit of the Lord leading me to return to Damascus before going to Jerusalem. It had now been three years since my encounter with Jesus on the road to Damascus, and I needed to return there to report on what Jesus had shown me during my time with Him.

Malchus agreed to accompany me on the ten-day journey. As we traveled, he told me about the many new leaders God had raised up in Gerasa. Our Lord was truly multiplying His church.

Although I did not know it then, I later learned King Aretas had continued to have his spies keep an eye on me. He still viewed me as a Jew who was stirring up his citizens. He had received the report about what happened to me in Pella. He had thought the crowd might eliminate his concerns by killing me. Unfortunately for him, the crowd had instead rallied around me.

He was growing concerned about how the Nabateans might react if he punished me. But then he heard I was headed to Damascus. I received word he had instructed the governor of Damascus to capture me. Aretas would have me removed as a possible threat while I was in Syria.

When Malchus and I arrived in Damascus, we first went to the home of Judas. He cordially greeted us and invited us to stay with him. Ananias, Nicanor, and the other leaders heard we were there and came to see us. Each day afterward, I was led by the Spirit of the Lord to preach throughout the city, and many believed. The Jewish leaders often attempted to debate me, but they were unable to refute my proofs that Jesus was indeed the Messiah.

. . .

Ananias quietly came to me and said my preaching had become much more powerful since he and I were last together. I explained what Jesus had taught me throughout my travels. I shared with him about the miracles of healing He had performed through me. I told him about all I had seen Him do among the people in Hippos, Gerasa, Philadelphia, Petra, and Pella. I recounted my time with Him on Mount Hermon and Mount Sinai.

I told him what Jesus had shown me regarding the Gentiles and that they were not to be burdened with meeting the requirements of the Mosaic Law. He agreed these matters needed to be resolved quickly before more division arose within the new church. Without question, it was time for me to go to Jerusalem and meet with Simon Peter and the others.

We found out the governor had posted guards at every gate with instructions to arrest me. We also learned the Jewish leaders were plotting to kill me. They, too, were watching for me day and night at the city gate so they could murder me. It was ironic that one group wanted to capture me for being a Jew and the other wanted to murder me for being an enemy of the Jews! It was clear I needed to find a way out of the city that avoided both groups. Nicanor and Ananias devised a plan for me to be let down inside a large basket through an opening in the city wall. The plan was successful, and it was several days before either group realized I had escaped.

I said goodbye to my friends, including Malchus. He was needed in Pella to continue his work there. The journey to Jerusalem was one for me to make alone. But then again, I would never be alone. Jesus would go with me.

* * *

11

When Saul arrived in Jerusalem, he tried to meet with the believers, but they were all afraid of him. They did not believe he had truly become a believer![1]

* * *

I was not the same man who had traveled this Damascus Road three years earlier. Before, I had been a disputer of Christ; now I was returning to Jerusalem as a disciple of Christ. My mission three years ago had been to prevent the spread of His Gospel. My mission now was to make His name known to the ends of the earth. I had once sought to see His followers destroyed; now I was seeking to see them multiplied, strengthened, and united.

The high priest and the others who had sent me on my mission were now aware I had abandoned their cause and become a follower of Jesus. And they were none too happy about it. They would not be welcoming me with open arms. But on the other hand, the believers in Jerusalem were probably not aware of the change in my life, so they would not be looking to welcome me, either. I spent most of my fourteen-day journey asking the Lord how He would have me navigate the hatred and distrust I knew I would encounter from both groups. Truth be told, I was more concerned about the reception I would receive from the church.

I expected that Caiaphas and the other religious leaders had still not taken any further action against the apostles. I was certain they would still be fearful of how the people might react if they did. So, I assumed the apostles would still be teaching and preaching outside the temple. But I also knew if I showed up at the temple, the high priest would have me arrested. I decided to send a message to the apostles to arrange a meeting with them. I needed a reliable messenger.

My other immediate need was a place to stay. I was not sure how my friend Mnason would receive me, but I believed the Spirit of the Lord was leading me to his home. Mnason looked surprised when I arrived at his door. Later that night, he told me he could tell I was a changed man the instant he saw me. "You no longer looked like a man who was warring against God," he said. "You now looked like a man who was humbly following God!"

We stayed awake late into the night as I recounted my experiences over the previous three years. I reminded him about the last thing he said to me before I left for Damascus: "Saul, I will pray that God will show you very clearly on this journey what He would have you do." I continued, "And my friend, by His grace He did just that! Now I must ask you, what has He shown you?"

"I am not yet certain if I believe whether Jesus was who He said He was," Mnason replied. "But I know the religious leaders were wrong in having Him put to death, and I know you were wrong in persecuting His followers. Soon after you finished your studies under Rabbi Gamaliel and returned to Tarsus, my cousin arrived from Cyprus. He became one of the followers of Jesus and traveled with Him for many months before His crucifixion. Time and again we have spoken over the years, and I have almost been persuaded by what he has told me. And now I must consider all you have told me as well, my friend. I think there is little more I need to hear. Allow me to ponder these things as we both rest tonight."

I replied with a smile, "Then tonight I will be the one asking God to show *you* very clearly what He would have you do!"

The next morning Mnason told me he had surrendered his life to Jesus and was now one of His followers. I told him he needed to be baptized and I would count it a privilege to be the one to do it. "But," I said, "I would like to do so in the presence of the other believers here in Jerusalem. To do that, I will need your help. Would you deliver a message to them that I have returned to Jerusalem, and I would like to meet with the apostles?"

Mnason confirmed they were still often seen teaching outside the temple. But when he delivered my message, it was clear the believers were afraid of me. They thought my message was a trick to trap them, and Mnason was one of my collaborators. They knew me before I left Jerusalem. And they knew I had left Jerusalem to persecute the believers in Damascus. They were well aware what I was capable of.

The believers, including the apostles, questioned whether I was even a believer, let alone that Jesus had called me to be an apostle. What right, they asked, did I have to call myself an apostle? I hadn't walked with Jesus – or so they thought. So, they told Mnason they would not meet with me or accept me into their fellowship.

But Mnason decided he would not be put off from his mission. He would do everything he could to arrange a meeting for me. He realized the best possibility was through his cousin Joseph – whom the apostles had nick-named Barnabas.

Like Mnason and me, Barnabas had been a talmid under the teaching of Rabbi Gamaliel. But in those days, he was known as Joseph. He had completed his studies the year before we began ours, but Mnason had introduced us at one point. Barnabas had later become a disciple of Jesus. He had followed Him during the months leading up to Jesus's crucifixion. He apparently was one of the followers gathered in an upper room when the Holy Spirit came upon them on the Day of Pentecost.

Because of the respect he had earned among the believers, he had become one of the early leaders of the church in Jerusalem. I thought it ironic I had never been given his name when I was seeking to arrest and punish the church leaders. Clearly, God had been protecting Barnabas.

Barnabas remembered that Mnason and I had been friends, so he was not surprised when Mnason told him I was staying at his home. He was, however, quite surprised to hear of the change that had taken place in my life. To his credit, Barnabas showed great faith and trust in God by being willing to meet with me.

He listened attentively as I recounted what had occurred in my life over the prior three years – including the mandate Jesus had given me to be the apostle to take His message to the Gentiles.

"Though I am the least deserving of all God's people," I said, *"He has graciously given me the privilege of telling the Gentiles about the endless treasures available to them in Christ."*(2)

As I watched his reaction, I could tell the Spirit of the Lord was easing his doubts. But when Mnason told him he believed me, and that through my witness the Spirit of the Lord had brought him to a place of salvation, the remainder of Barnabas's apprehension disappeared. Together, we all rejoiced in the goodness and mercy of God. Then Barnabas reached out to me, put his arm around me, and drew me close like a brother.

. . .

Barnabas went to the apostles on my behalf and advocated for them to meet with me. Though he told them I was a changed man, several were still skeptical. Finally, they decided I would only meet with Peter and James, the half brother of Jesus. I knew James, like the rest of his brothers, had not acknowledged Jesus as Savior until after His resurrection. But from that day forward, the brothers had followed Him with their whole hearts. James and his younger brother Jude were now influential leaders within the Jerusalem church.

Peter and James had many questions for me, as did I for them – so we began our time by getting acquainted. In addition to telling them about my encounter with Jesus on the road to Damascus, I told them about the many believers I had met since then. Simon Peter was intrigued to hear about Enos and Malchus, and how the Spirit of the Lord was working through them among the new believers in the cities of the Decapolis.

"I remember the day Jesus delivered Enos from the demons that possessed him," Peter said. "We had sailed across the sea the night before. A storm had arisen, and we thought we were all going to die. Jesus had simply told the winds and the waves to be still, and suddenly there was great calm.

"After such an event-filled journey, we expected Jesus to perform many miracles that next day and preach to large crowds of people along the shore. But He only spoke to one man – Enos. And after He delivered Enos, He told us to get back into the boat. We needed to return to Capernaum.

"I recall thinking we had traveled a long way for Jesus to see only one man. Months later, when Jesus taught about leaving the ninety-nine to go rescue the one, I thought of that day … and I thought about Enos.

"When we left Enos on the shore that day, Jesus had told him, '*Go home to your friends and tell them how much the Lord has done for you, and how He has had mercy on you.*'"[3] Peter was now overjoyed to hear how Enos had done just that!

. . .

But when I told them about Malchus, Peter began to weep. After he regained his composure, Peter said, "My only time with Malchus was at a moment of great fear that night in the garden. We were surrounded by guards with swords, clubs, and spears. We had been abruptly awakened and were startled by their arrival in the middle of the night. Jesus had been telling us for days that the hour would come, but we hadn't really believed Him. And I had been the one who boasted that I was prepared to follow Him to the death.

"But when it came down to it, my only act had been to lash out at a servant and sever his ear. Jesus rebuked me and told me to put away my sword. Then he knelt in front of the man and healed the man's ear. It wasn't until much later I learned that his name was Malchus. While Jesus was still kneeling before him with His hand on his ear, I ran away like the rest of the disciples. I ran out of fear. I was confused. I was embarrassed by Jesus's rebuke. And I was remorseful over my actions.

"Until this very moment, I had never considered the possibility Jesus would use even my impetuous act for His greater mission. I saw Malchus as an enemy. Jesus saw him as one of His sheep in need of salvation. I saw him for the moment, whereas Jesus saw him as one He would work through in the days ahead to make His name known among the people of the Decapolis. Where I saw an enemy, Jesus saw a disciple in the making. That shouldn't surprise me – because that's the way Jesus always saw me – even from our very first meeting."

Over the next fifteen days, I continued to tell Peter, James, and Barnabas about the work God had done in my life over the previous three years. They marveled at the truth Jesus had revealed to me – truths that to the best of their knowledge Jesus had only revealed to His apostles. It confirmed for all of us that the message of salvation I was preaching had not come by human reasoning or logic, rather by direct revelation from Jesus Himself.

. . .

I went on to tell them about the forty days I had spent with Jesus on Mount Sinai and all He had shown me regarding the Gentile believers. I shared that just as Jesus had given Peter the responsibility of building up His church among the Jews, He had given *me* the responsibility of doing so among the Gentiles. However, that was not to say that Peter was not to bring the Good News to the Gentiles, or I was not to do so to the Jews. Jesus had called us all to be witnesses to all people! At the end of our time together, Peter and James were convinced of the veracity of my testimony and the genuineness of my transformation, as well as my apostleship. While we may not have agreed on all matters concerning the church, we were in complete agreement on the Good News of the Gospel of salvation.

For the remainder of our time together, I joined them in going throughout the city preaching boldly in the name of the Lord. Many of the Jews began to recognize me. The Hellenistic Jews – those who had participated in the trial and death of Stephen – remembered me as one who had been one of them. They began to debate me, and I began to sense a need to take up the witness of Stephen in whose death I had been so complicit.

It quickly became apparent the Jews were making plans to murder me. But, at the same time, Jesus made it abundantly clear – again – that He had other plans for me. One day, while I was praying in the temple, I fell into a trance. I saw a vision of Jesus saying to me, *"Hurry! Leave Jerusalem, for the people here won't accept your testimony about Me."*

"But Lord," I argued, *"they certainly know that in every synagogue I imprisoned and beat those who believed in You. And I was in complete agreement when Your witness Stephen was killed. I stood by and kept the coats they took off when they stoned him."* But the Lord said to me, *"Go, for I will send you far away to the Gentiles!"*(4)

Knowing the threat against me, Peter and James decided it was time for me to leave. Jesus had given me an assignment elsewhere, and I must quickly return to Tarsus. We heard the Jews were watching for me along the road to Jaffa, fully expecting me to depart for home through that port.

Instead, Barnabas and a few other believers would help me travel to Caesarea; I would depart from there.

But there was one thing left for me to do first. I invited Mnason to join Peter, James, Barnabas, and me at one of the mikvehs (ritual cleansing pools) outside of the temple. There I had the privilege of baptizing my good friend as he declared his faith in Jesus the Messiah. Barnabas watched with great joy as he witnessed his cousin being baptized. He and I now had yet another bond drawing us closer – the salvation of Mnason.

Barnabas, in fact, had become like a brother. He walked with me every step of the way to Caesarea without any concern for his own safety. He had urged the apostles to receive me. He had stood by my side when the Jews were debating me, and now he was bravely accompanying me on my journey. He was there with me – encouraging me each step of the way. There was no question why he had been given the name Barnabas, meaning the "son of encouragement." He truly was to me!

As I boarded the ship in Caesarea, I turned and waved at Barnabas. There was little doubt in my mind we would see one another again. Somehow, I knew our time together had only just begun.

* * *

12

When the believers heard about this, they took him down to Caesarea and sent him away to Tarsus, his hometown.[1]

* * *

It was autumn when I departed the docks at Caesarea Maritima on a Cilician ship bound for Tarsus. We were due to make port in a little more than four days at our intermediate stop of Salamis on the island of Cyprus. We would hold over there for a day or two while the captain and crew unloaded cargo and took on additional goods bound for Tarsus. It would take us an additional five days to make port in Tarsus.

The skies were clear, and the seas were calm as we sailed north along the coastline past Tyre. When the city of Berytus came into view, the captain steered his ship out toward open seas in the direction of Cyprus. Along the way, the Lord granted me many opportunities to tell my fellow passengers and the crew about Jesus. Some of the crew had heard His name, but most knew little about Him. I was able to share how He had called out to me on the road to Damascus and how He had redeemed me from my sin. A few of the crew and passengers became believers.

. . .

Two days out into open seas we began to encounter high waves and strong winds from the southeast. As the day continued, the winds increased to typhoon strength and the waves were breaking above the ship's bow. I could tell the captain and crew were worried. We were still a day away from Cyprus in good weather, but the wind and seas were working against us. Salamis, however, was the closest port, so the captain made the decision to press forward.

Soon the skies turned dark, and the deck began to be pelted by heavy rain. The captain gave the order to strike the sails and batten down the ship to weather the storm. The waters were too deep for the ship's anchors to do any good; we continued to be tossed by the sea. The crew banded the ship with heavy ropes to strengthen the hull. The other passengers and I assisted the crew as best we could.

After the work was finished, we huddled under a covering to escape the driving rain. As we sat there, I told everyone the story I had recently heard from Peter about the storm Jesus had stilled. I called out to Him in prayer and asked Him to still this storm and keep each one of us from harm. "Lord," I said, "I know You have more for me to do. And I believe that is true for each one of us on this ship. So, we will trust You to bring us through this storm to a safe haven."

When morning arrived, the storm was still raging. But we were encouraged when one of the sailors announced he could see land in the distance. The crew began to take depth soundings. The water was now 30 meters deep. The captain had the crew set the foresail and rudder in place so he could attempt to steer the ship toward the shore. Everyone on board seemed hopeful now that land was within sight. Suddenly, the ship struck rocks hidden just below the surface. The bow splintered from the impact and the ship began to take on water.

The crew lowered the lifeboat for us to escape the sinking ship. But just then, the stern abruptly came about in the waves, smashing the lifeboat against the rocks. All that remained were pieces of splintered wood. The ship's captain called out for us to abandon ship.

Once in the water, we each strapped ourselves to a piece of the broken ship or lifeboat to help us stay afloat. We used ropes we had brought from the ship to band our flotilla of castaways together. The waves tossed us hither and yon. Though we knew there was land in sight, we quickly realized we did not have enough strength to reach it. The captain shouted to us to conserve our energy for when it could make a difference.

The storm continued to rage throughout the day and into the night. We all began to shiver as the temperatures fell. I was exhausted and my body demanded sleep, but I knew I needed to keep myself awake. If any of us fell asleep, we would slip below the water. I decided the best thing to do was lift our voices – and what better way than singing praises to our Lord. My voice was raspy from the water and weak from exhaustion, but I began to sing as loud as I could. After a few minutes, I heard the voice of another man. Soon, we were joined by another … and then another. In a short while, our voices seemed to grow stronger as we sang praises to Jesus. This group of Gentile sailors and passengers began to sound like a heavenly choir.

I don't know how long we sang, but we were still glorifying God when the sun began to dawn, and the wind and waves began to calm. We gratefully realized the waves and current had pushed us closer to shore. The Lord gave us the strength to kick and swim the rest of the way. By midday we had made it to dry land – all of us! We offered up prayers of thanksgiving to God, and many more of the men surrendered their lives to Jesus that day!

We were only a short distance from Salamis, so after recovering our strength, we made our way along the shore by foot. We all remained in Salamis for two days while our ship's captain arranged passage for us on another ship bound for Tarsus. He and his crew went about gathering whatever cargo was recoverable from the wreckage of their ship.

• • •

Our time in Salamis gave all of us an occasion to tell our story of how God had protected us. He hadn't kept us *from* the storm. He hadn't chosen to *still* the storm. But He had most definitely kept us *through* the storm!

The five-day journey from Salamis to Tarsus was uneventful as we sailed across calm seas. No one was on the docks to greet me when I arrived; none of my family or friends was aware of my journey. So, after I said goodbye to my fellow passengers, I set off to my family home.

Dinah and Reuben greeted me warmly when they discovered me standing at their door. My nephew, Hezron, now eight years old, had grown so much I barely recognized him. And their family had grown with the addition of their daughter, Esther, who was now two.

In the days following, I told them about all my experiences since I had last seen them. I told them about my zealous persecution of the church up until the day Jesus called out to me on the road to Damascus. I told them about my travels that followed – my imprisonment, the attempts on my life, and my most recent shipwreck. But most importantly, I told them the Good News of Jesus and about seeing people's lives transformed by God's saving grace. Even Hezron sat at my feet, captivated by every story and every detail. My heart rejoiced when Reuben, Dinah, and Hezron all surrendered their lives to Jesus.

They updated me on all the news about Tarsus. God had graciously enabled our family's tent-making business to prosper under Reuben's leadership. He was becoming recognized as a successful tradesman and was gaining influence in the city. Tarsus itself was continuing to prosper and expand as more people migrated to the city from other parts of the Roman empire.

A few days later, I set out to visit my close friends. The first one was Arsakes. He had recently been named a city magistrate, following in his father's footsteps. He wore the influence and power of the position well. I had always considered him a strong leader, demonstrating a heart to serve others. He listened with interest as I relayed my experiences. It was obvious the Lord had gone before me and prepared Arsakes's heart for what I was sharing. Before our time together was over, Arsakes became a follower of Jesus.

He asked me to come to his home the next day so I could share the Good News with everyone in his household. They also listened intently, and when I was finished, they surrendered their lives to Jesus. That afternoon we all went to the shoreline of the Cydnus River where I baptized them. Arsakes asked if I would come each night and teach his family and servants what they must now do as followers of Jesus. I told him I would if they invited their friends and neighbors to join them. Every night the gatherings grew. Soon we had outgrown their home and were meeting in the surrounding courtyard.

The next friend I went to visit was Ashmus. He was now a respected teacher at the most acclaimed university in Tarsus, rivaling those in Athens and Alexandria. He had most recently assisted his mentor, Lucius Annaeus Cornutus, in compiling a collection of Greek theology. It didn't take long for him to start debating me. When I told him about my personal encounter with Jesus, the Son of the Living God, he immediately attempted to refute everything I was saying.

"Ashmus," I said, "you have been debating the existence of the one true Jehovah God with me since we were young boys in school. But in your own beliefs, you worship one whom you call the Unknown God. *This God, whom you worship without knowing, is the one I'm telling you about.*

"He is the God who made the world and everything in it. Since He is Lord of heaven and earth, He doesn't live in man-made temples, and human hands can't serve His needs – like the gods you worship – *for He has no needs. He himself gives life and breath to everything, and He satisfies every need. From one man He created all the nations throughout the whole earth. He decided beforehand when they should rise and fall, and he determined their boundaries.*

. . .

"His purpose was for the nations to seek after Him and perhaps feel their way toward Him and find Him – though He is not far from any one of us. For in Him we live and move and exist. As some of your own poets have said, 'We are His offspring.'"[(2)]

"I have believed these things since I was a child," I continued. "He has shown me that He *overlooked people's ignorance about these things in earlier times, but now He commands everyone everywhere to repent of their sins and turn to Him. For He has set a day for judging the world with justice by the Man He has appointed* – the One I have told you about whose name is Jesus – *and He proved to everyone who this is by raising Him from the dead."*[(3)]

"When I returned to Jerusalem almost four years ago, I denied that Jesus was that Man. I persecuted others for following Him. But by His grace, He still had mercy on me and sought me out. He extends that same mercy and grace to you, Ashmus, if you will receive it."

Ashmus silently stared at me for a few moments before he replied, "Paul, you have become even more articulate since we last debated. And I can see you wholeheartedly believe all you have said to be true. But I am not persuaded. Do not waste more of our time trying to convince me, we must simply agree to disagree."

That wasn't the first time I had heard someone reject the Good News, and it most certainly would not be the last. But my heart was broken to hear those words spoken by my friend. I told him I would pray that God would open his eyes as He had opened mine. We parted that day without my knowing if I would ever see him again.

Two days later, I visited my friend Benjamin. As you will recall, he is a Sadducee – which means he does not believe in the resurrection of the dead. So, the very idea I had an encounter with the resurrected Jesus immediately prompted him to reject everything I said. Unlike Ashmus, he not only rejected the truth, but he also made it clear that anyone who believed the statements I was making was a heretic and a blasphemer. Then he tore his robes and demanded I leave his presence. "Furthermore," he said, "you are not welcome in the synagogue here in Tarsus. If you attempt to speak these lies to our people, I will personally see to it you are punished! From this day forward you are dead to me – you are my enemy and an enemy of all Jews!"

Again, I left grieving for another friend as I walked back to Arsakes's home. After these experiences, I was looking forward to sharing the truth with a group of people whose hearts were receptive. That was the night I met a physician who would become not only a lifelong friend but also one of my most trusted companions in ministry.

Luke grew up in the city of Antioch in Syria and had come to Tarsus on business. During his work affairs, he met Arsakes who invited Luke to come to his home to hear the most astounding truth. Luke was familiar with Greek theology. He had grown up hearing about Hercules, the son of Zeus. So initially, my statements about Jesus being the Son of God didn't impress him. As he later told me, "I knew all about the self-centered, demanding, egotistical deities who had come to earth. But when you told me you had encountered this Jesus personally while traveling to Damascus to persecute His followers, I decided to listen to you.

"But as impressive as your personal experiences were, I became even more intrigued by your stories about this Man called Jesus. This Son of God had spoken of a God who loved me. He had been sent by His Father to walk and live in this world – not to oppress us like the gods I knew – but to set us free! His mission had ultimately led to His death – not for His actions, but for mine!

"And then you said this Jesus had not remained in the grave; He had risen so we might have abundant life! I came to the realization that you Christ-followers didn't worship a myth, or a god made of stone – you worshiped a living Savior. And you were willing to be imprisoned or die for your belief! I had never known anyone willing to die for Zeus! You followers were compelled to tell everyone about Jesus, and I had never witnessed such conviction in anyone else!"

That night Luke became a follower of Jesus – and he never looked back!

The next night as I arrived at Arsakes's home, he took me aside to tell me Ashmus and Benjamin had visited him. Though they had come to see him separately, they both had come with a similar complaint – about me. They told Arsakes I was stirring up people with false teachings. Arsakes attempted to convince both men my teachings were not false, but his words fell on deaf ears. They quickly realized he had also become a follower of Jesus, which caused them to leave abruptly.

But Arsakes continued, "Ashmus will complain about you to anyone who will listen, but it is Benjamin who worries me. Before he realized I am also now a follower of Jesus, he had begun to tell me how some of the Jews were plotting to silence you. He said he had come to me to prevent unnecessary bloodshed. He suggested that I as a magistrate could demand you either stop preaching your message or leave Tarsus. He didn't seem to care which it was, as long as you stopped preaching. But when he realized I believed in Jesus, too, he muttered they would have to pursue other options.

"Paul, I fear the Jews are making plans to harm you – or perhaps, even kill you! I think it would be wise for you to leave the city for a while and give them time to cool off. Reuben, Dinah, and I, together with some of the other believers, can continue the work you have begun here. Benjamin and the other Jews who want to do you harm will not be so foolish as to attempt any action against me or your family. They know the entire city would turn against them if they did."

. . .

That night as I asked the Lord what He would have me do, He told me my work in Tarsus was complete; it was time for me to go to another city. I remained in Tarsus one more day so I could say farewell to the believers at the nightly gathering.

Before our time began that night, Luke told me he would be returning to Antioch the next morning – his business in Tarsus had concluded. I told him I was also leaving and planned to head east to the city of Aegeae. Luke told me he would be passing through Aegeae, so we agreed to travel together.

The next morning, after saying farewell to Arsakes and my family, Luke and I set out on our journey.

* * *

13

After that visit I went north into the provinces of Syria and Cilicia.[1]

* * *

As Luke and I traveled, I knew God had ordained these three days so I could share more of the teachings of Jesus. Luke's physician's mind absorbed the details of everything I told him, and his insatiable questioning probed for even more. I realized he had a thorough understanding of the events leading up to the crucifixion and resurrection of Jesus as best I knew them – as well as the birth of the church since His ascension. Perhaps the Spirit of the Lord would use him in the days ahead to record those truths for all to know and understand.

When we arrived at Aegeae along the Bay of Issus, Luke booked passage on a ferry and continued his journey home to Antioch. I challenged him to be faithful in telling others in his city about Jesus. I had no idea how our paths would cross in the days ahead – but somehow, I knew they would.

Aegeae is a much smaller city than Tarsus; but as a port city along the bay, it had become one of the gateway cities into Asia from the east. Arsakes had heard a small enclave of Jews lived in the city – as well as an even smaller gathering of believers – but he did not know anything about their leaders. I knew the Lord wanted me to go to the synagogue and talk about Jesus before I went anywhere else.

The rabbi invited me to share a word of greeting and address those gathered. Unbeknownst to me, a man named Timon was in the group, and he was not pleased to see me. He had made his way to Aegeae from Jerusalem four years earlier because of me. But as he listened to my story, he began to silently praise God. Timon was one of the men chosen to serve the Hellenistic widows in the church of Jerusalem. He had been one of the men I intended to arrest. But the Lord had led him to leave the city before that happened.

Since arriving in Aegeae, he had quietly shared about Jesus with a small but growing number of acquaintances. He was always fearful of being too vocal or too visible in this small city. The people who had come to faith in Jesus thus far were Jews – so though they were Christ-followers, they had also continued their former religious practices as part of the Jewish community. This meant they really had not created a stir among the people.

This was not the case when I stood up and told my story in the synagogue. Some of the people asked questions, but others began to say I was speaking blasphemy. I concluded my time by quoting the prophet Habakkuk:

"Brothers, listen! I am *here to proclaim that through this Man Jesus there is forgiveness for your sins. Everyone who believes in Him is made right in God's sight – something the law of Moses could never do. Be careful! Don't let the prophets' words apply to you. For they said,*
'Look, you mockers, be amazed and die!
For I am doing something in your own day,
something you wouldn't believe even if someone told you about it.'"(2)

. . .

Many in the crowd asked me to return the following week and speak more about these things. Several men followed me as I left, and we continued in conversation. One of them remained with me after all the others had gone their way. When he said his name was Timon, it still did not register who he was. But I listened intently as he told me how he had been one of the 3,000 people who believed in Christ the day Peter preached in Jerusalem. When he informed me he was one of the men selected to serve the church in Jerusalem, I realized I had once been the enemy of this man who was now my brother.

I stopped walking, turned to him, and said, "Brother, please forgive me – for the threats I made against you, and for the actions I took against your brothers. I can never make amends to you for what I have done; but, by His mercy and grace, God has forgiven me and cleansed me. I ask you to forgive me – not because I deserve it, nor because Christ commands we forgive, but because of the love we have for one another through the same Spirit who dwells within us both."

Timon's response reflected the purity of his faith in Christ. He said, "I need not forgive you now, because I forgave you long ago. Jesus taught His disciples:

'If you forgive those who sin against you, your heavenly Father will forgive you. But if you refuse to forgive others, your Father will not forgive your sins.'[3]

"I do not want anything in my heart that separates me from the Father's love or from *His* forgiveness. So today, I rejoice in the good news of what Jesus has done in your heart and that we are now brothers in Him."

His sincerity and purity of heart humbled me, and I knew Jesus had much to teach me through Timon. I asked if he knew of a place I could lodge, and without hesitation he invited me to stay with him.

. . .

Throughout the week, Timon invited other Jewish believers in the city to come and meet with me. During our time together, I noticed they were timid about sharing their faith with others. They had allowed themselves to be confined by their former practices under the law of Moses.

I said to them, "*The old way, with laws etched in stone, led to death, though it began with such glory that the people of Israel could not bear to look at Moses' face. For his face shone with the glory of God, even though the brightness was already fading away. If the old way, which brings condemnation, was glorious, how much more glorious is the new way, which makes us right with God! In fact, that first glory was not glorious at all compared with the overwhelming glory of the new way.*[4]

"*Since this new way gives us such confidence, we can be very bold. For the Lord is the Spirit, and wherever the Spirit of the Lord is, there is freedom. So all of us who have had* the veil of sin *removed can see and reflect the glory of the Lord. And the Lord – who is the Spirit – makes us more and more like* Jesus *as we are changed into His glorious image.*[5]

"So, as Jesus said, '*Do not hide your light under a basket, rather, place it on a stand for all to see,*'[6] so that His glory is seen, and His Good News is heard."

I went on to tell them the Good News was not only for the Jews, but it was also for the Gentiles as well. I admonished them to shine their light among all people. Some of them resisted at first. But I explained this was part of the reason the Spirit of the Lord had scattered His people from Jerusalem in all directions. I reminded them that when God entered into His covenant with Abraham, He had declared, "*All the nations of the earth will be blessed.*"[7]

. . .

The following Sabbath, I returned to the synagogue with Timon. This time there was a much larger crowd. Some had returned with more questions. Some had come out of curiosity. Others had come prepared to debate me while several had come to discredit me and the truths I was proclaiming.

After a while I saw one of the rabbis slip away. He soon returned with three Roman soldiers. He pointed to me and abruptly announced, "This is the man who has intruded into our synagogue and disrupted our meeting. He is promoting the teachings of a Man named Jesus who the Roman prefect of Iudaea sentenced to be crucified. That Man was found guilty of teaching insurrection against the emperor, and this man is doing the same thing. Arrest him and do to him what is appropriate under our laws!"

Despite protests from some in the crowd, the soldiers bound my arms behind me and led me to their fortress. Timon and a few others followed and continued to protest, but to no avail. The soldier in charge turned to them and said, "If you continue your rantings about this man, we will happily permit you to partake in the same fate!" I told Timon and the men to be quiet as there was nothing to be gained by their continued attempts to intervene.

Aegeae was designated a free city by Rome, so it enjoys a certain degree of autonomy. But it also houses a small fortress. No Roman prefect has been assigned to the city, so the soldiers are charged with the responsibility of meting out Roman justice. As I quickly learned, the garrison's commander defined Roman justice as Roman punishment. That meant I was not to receive a trial or a hearing, I would simply be punished based on the false charges brought by my accusers.

When the soldiers stripped away my cloak, they immediately saw I was not a novice to being scourged. I think that fact increased their resolve that I was guilty and deserved to be punished. When I announced I was a Roman citizen who was due a fair trial, the commander smiled. "You have been heard, citizen," he said, "and you have been found guilty!"

• • •

The commander then instructed his soldiers to carry out the scourging with a vengeance. I fell unconscious before they were finished. I don't know how much time passed before the pain of my injuries woke me up, but I found myself lying on the dirt floor of a dingy, dark cell somewhere in the fortress.

I was never given anything to treat my wounds, so it was no surprise they became infected; I was burning with fever within days. Throughout it all, the Spirit of the Lord was my comfort. He eased my pain and eventually took away my fever. Seeing that I wasn't going to die, the soldiers began to bring me a meager ration of food and water each day.

One soldier was more attentive than the others. We eventually struck up a conversation. It was limited at first, but as the days passed, we talked more and more. I learned his name was Marius, and he also was from Tarsus. He told me all the soldiers had expected me to die in that cell. In fact, they had cast lots over how quickly I would die. They were amazed when I began to recover. He said the gods must be with me.

I explained that my God *was* with me. As I told him my story over the next few days, he began to ask more and more questions about Jesus – who He was, and why I was willing to be punished for His sake. Marius told me he believed in the gods, but he wasn't willing to be beaten for any of them.

I told him that none of his gods had ever taken his punishment in his place. None of his gods had ever died on a cross for his sins … but Jesus had. Jesus had died for my sins and for Marius's sins. But He had not remained dead. He had risen from the grave and conquered death. It was His Spirit who had led me to Aegeae. It was His Spirit who had enabled me to endure the scourging and survive its aftermath. It was His Spirit who had led the two of us to meet and talk about Him.

"Marius," I said, "Jesus has gone to a lot of effort so you might hear the Good News and be saved." Marius believed in Jesus that day. Whenever he was able, he would come and spend time with me. I had no idea how long I would be in that cell, but I spent each moment I could teaching him about Jesus.

Eventually he convinced the commander to allow me to have visitors. He even carried word for me to Timon to let him know to come see me. My conditions began to improve that day. Timon was permitted to bring me another cloak to replace the one that had been torn to shreds. He also was allowed to bring along some papyrus and a quill so he could write some of my words of encouragement for the believers in the city. I was pleased to learn the believers had become bolder in their witness and their number was increasing – both Jew and Gentile alike. Marius soon began to join them in worship.

One day the commander of the fortress came to me. "Paul," he said, "you have been in here for nine months. During that time the city has begun to change. There are a growing number of people who believe as you do. But rather than promoting rebellion, they are model citizens treating everyone fairly and serving others. Your God has made a difference in their lives, and I have become convinced you were falsely accused. So, I am releasing you from this place. You are free to go – but I caution you that the men who originally accused you will still try and do you harm. I suggest you leave this city because I do not believe I will be able to protect you."

Timon was surprised to see me when I arrived at his home. I spent the next few days there meeting with the believers. But the Spirit of the Lord showed me it was time to leave. Timon, Marius, and others would continue the work. I was still in a somewhat weakened state, so Timon offered to make the two-day journey with me north to Anazarbus.

We set off the next morning. The road to Anazarbus was a sparsely traveled trade route. Merchants would use it to drive their caravans northward from the port of Aegeae with goods from all over the world. But since Aegeae was a smaller port, it was used less frequently. As Timon and

I were walking, we did not come upon anyone else – until we found ourselves surrounded by a band of robbers.

It was easy to see we were not transporting any treasures. And our clothing was evidence we were not wealthy men. I was surprised they chose to stop us, but we must have been the first people to pass that way for some time. They demanded that we give them all we had. However, when they discovered how little that was, they became frustrated and began to beat us.

When we regained consciousness just before sunset, all we had in our possession were the cloaks on our backs. The robbers had taken our change of clothing, our sandals, and our sack of food. Thankfully, God had protected us from any further harm, and the robbers were nowhere in sight. Our bruised bodies ached from the beatings, but neither of us had any broken bones. We decided to stay there and rest for the night. There was no sense in attempting to travel any farther in the dark.

Timon and I thanked God for His mercy and began to sing praises to His name until weariness overtook us and we fell asleep. We didn't know if the robbers were still nearby, but we could only imagine the look on their faces if they were watching two bruised and beaten men singing songs of praise after what we had experienced. We prayed that if the men could hear us, the Spirit of the Lord would use the words of our songs to bring them to faith in Jesus.

* * *

14

I have traveled on many long journeys. I have faced danger from rivers and from robbers. I have faced danger from my own people, the Jews, as well as from the Gentiles. I have faced danger in the cities, in the deserts, and on the seas.[1]

* * *

The next morning, Timon and I set out on our journey again – only this time we were walking barefooted, which slowed our progress somewhat. But the Spirit of the Lord lifted our hearts and we arrived in Anazarbus by nightfall.

The city is an acropolis, built upon a lofty, isolated hill with steep sides. It was originally established by the Assyrians because of its strong defensible location. It overlooked a narrow passage that led into Cappadocia. That passage became known as the Cilician Gates during the invasion of Alexander the Great. Today under Roman rule, it is not seen as having significant military importance, but it is considered a gateway outpost of trade into the northeastern regions. In my tentmaking years, I had supplied many Tarsian tents to a merchant named Arsames in Anazarbus, who in turn sold them in Cappadocia, Bithynia, and Armenia.

. . .

I decided to look up Arsames to see if he could recommend lodging. I was certain he would be well-known in the city. Arsames is the kind of man you can't forget. Since I am not a very tall man, it is rare to find someone who is shorter than I am. But such is the case with Arsames; however, his girth almost equals his height. He has a jovial personality that seems to complement his round physical shape. And I was correct – the first person we asked was able to direct us to his home.

His eyes immediately lit up when he opened the door. Before I realized it, he had reached out and drawn me close in an embrace. After a few minutes of introductions and pleasantries, I asked if he could recommend a place for us to stay for the night. "Yes," he answered without any hesitation, "you can stay here with me!"

A few days later, we learned there was a caravan preparing to head to Aegeae. I knew Timon needed to return to the city so he could continue his work, but I was hesitant to send him on the journey alone. I feared that he might again be fallen upon by the robbers we had encountered. However, the sheer size of this caravan would be a deterrent, and I knew this was God's provision so Timon could return home safely.

Before Timon departed, Arsames had already become a fellow believer in Christ. As I shared my testimony and the story of redemption that is available to us all through the shed blood of Jesus, Arsames never hesitated. He wept as he asked Jesus to forgive him of his sins, and he praised Jesus with equal passion for paying the price for his sins. As I think back over the years, God has granted me the privilege of seeing many who have come to faith in Jesus – some immediately and some over time. But I don't believe I have ever seen anyone who surrendered his life to Christ with a deeper commitment or a more genuine enthusiasm than the Gentile by the name of Arsames.

Very quickly his wife, Isabella, his son, Thoros, and all his household became believers as well – and their collective joy was contagious. Our nightly gatherings with his friends and neighbors continued to grow. I had discovered early on there were no Jews living in this city, which meant the people coming to faith came from a pagan Gentile background. There was a hunger and thirst like I had never seen. The Spirit of the Lord was working mightily in this acropolis. It was quickly becoming a city like Jesus had once described: *"You are the light of the world – like a city on a hilltop that cannot be hidden."*(2)

Six months after my arrival, Jesus showed me that my work there was finished, and it was time for me to move on. I knew God would use Arsames and the others to continue the work there in Anazarbus.

Arsames told me about his brother, Servilius, who lived farther north in the city of Hierapolis. I sensed the Lord prompting me to go there, so I immediately set out on my journey. Arsames sent Thoros to accompany me and to introduce me to his brother.

Hierapolis lies in the valley of the Pyramus River, in the shadow of a fortress that towers above on another steep-sided hill. Over the years, the city has been considered part of the province of Cilicia, as it is now by the Romans, but at other times it has been part of Cappadocia. The Romans recently renamed the city, which was formerly called Castabala. The new name, Hierapolis, is the name of another well-known spa on the sea, and evidently Rome intends to turn this city into a similar resort on the river. The city has undergone quite a bit of renovation in recent years, giving it a typical Roman appearance.

The axis of the city is a colonnaded street bordered by majestic columns. The city boasts several new bathhouses, a newly constructed theater, and a recent temple built to the goddess Artemis.

As soon as we arrived at the home of Servilius, I could easily see he and Arsames were brothers. They shared many of the same features, including their stature and girth. They also shared their gregarious nature. As soon as Thoros made introductions, Servilius welcomed me into his life without reservation. Within a matter of two days, I had the joy of baptizing him as a testimony to his newfound faith in Jesus. To the best of my knowledge, he was the first follower of Jesus in his city – but I had no doubts he would not be the last.

I stayed in Servilius's home from the day I arrived until the day I left. It wasn't long before his wife, children, business associates, and servants had all followed in his footsteps and surrendered their lives to Jesus. This was the second city where I could not identify any Jewish residents, but the Gospel was flowing freely among the Gentiles. I encountered little resistance throughout the three months I was there. Each day more people believed and were baptized.

The priests of the temple to Artemis went to the governor to complain I was turning people against the gods of their fathers. Each day their numbers – and the offerings to their temple – were dwindling. But the governor saw the change taking place among his citizens was for the better. He visited Servilius and me to share how his city was becoming more peaceable and more loving toward one another. He could only attribute the change to the fact that many of the people were becoming followers of Jesus. "If the Jesus you follow can change the hearts of the people in such a way," he told us, "I do not want to be left out. Tell me how I, too, can become a follower of Jesus!"

Even the Roman soldiers in the fortress overlooking the city began to take notice, and many of them came to faith. I had never seen the power of the Gospel transform a city and a people in such a way. I prayed this city would not be an exception – and it would become a shining light that multiplied throughout the surrounding cities and beyond.

Three months after I arrived, I felt the Lord again leading me to move on. I challenged Servilius and the other believers to go out into the surrounding areas including Cappadocia, Armenia, Pontus, and Bithynia. By the time I left, they had already sent out twelve men to go in pairs into six different cities. The believers in Hierapolis knew God had not given them the Good News to keep to themselves!

Thoros accompanied me as the Spirit of the Lord led us to turn toward the southwest and travel to the coastal city of Seleucia. The two-week journey was uneventful, and it provided me with valuable time to better equip Thoros for his leadership role in the church in Anazarbus. I also challenged him to report all we had witnessed in Hierapolis to the church. They needed to follow the example of their new brothers and sisters and passionately go outside of their city to share the Good News about Jesus with those who had not yet heard.

Seleucia, with its more moderate climate, reminded me of my home city of Tarsus. The city is located a few kilometers upriver from the mouth of the Calycadnus River where it flows into the Mediterranean Sea. Though the port is much smaller than Tarsus, it serves as a gateway for goods into the western corner of Cilicia.

We arrived shortly before the Sabbath, so we quickly located lodging for the night and got settled in before the sun set. The next morning, we visited the local synagogue. When I mentioned to the rabbi I had been taught by Rabbi Gamaliel, he immediately invited me to speak to those gathered.

"My young friend, Thoros, and I are fellow countrymen from Cilicia," I began. "We are here to bring you Good News. God's promise to our ancestors has come to pass in our time. The promised Savior of Israel has come, and His name is Jesus." I then proceeded to walk them through the promises in the Scriptures and the reality of how each one had been fulfilled in Jesus.

When I was done, I said, *"Brothers, listen! We are here to proclaim that through this Man Jesus there is forgiveness for your sins. Everyone who believes in Him is made right in God's sight – something the law of Moses could never do."*(3)

. . .

Some of the Jews and godly converts to Judaism became believers that day. When Thoros and I left the synagogue, they followed us asking what they must now do. One of the men asked if I knew a man named Procorus. "Procorus," he said, "speaks of this Man Jesus the same way you do. He also spent time in Jerusalem until he was forced to leave the city. Since then, he has traveled around this corner of Cilicia telling people about this Man."

I asked where he was now. "He is here in Seleucia," the man replied. "I can take you to him."

My mind started to race. Was he one of the seven leaders of the church in Jerusalem I had attempted to arrest and persecute? Had he traveled to Cilicia to evade me just like Timon had done? If so, I needed to speak with him and ask forgiveness.

I had never met Procorus before, but I could tell by the strained expression on his face he knew exactly who I was. He began to relax as the man who had brought us introduced me by sharing how I had spoken in the synagogue.

Procorus extended his hand in greeting and said, "Welcome! At first, I thought you were someone else, but obviously I was mistaken."

"No, you were correct," I said. "I was Saul the persecutor, but I am no longer he." I explained how Jesus had come to me on the road to Damascus. I continued, "*I am the least deserving of all God's people, and yet He has graciously given me the privilege of telling* all people, including *the Gentiles, about the endless treasures available to them in Christ.*[(4)]

. . .

"Procorus, I stand before you as a man whose sins have been washed away by the shed blood of Jesus. He has forgiven me of my sins, and I ask you to do the same. Forgive me for the threats I made against you and for the harm I brought to your brothers and sisters in Christ."

He remained silent for a time, and I knew he was asking the Lord for wisdom in how to respond. Were my statements genuine, or was this merely a ploy on my part? Though no words were spoken aloud, my spirit could hear the conversation taking place within him. Like his brothers, he was filled by the Spirit with grace and truth. In a few moments, he took my hand and embraced me, called me his brother, and told me he forgave me. "What's more," he said, "the Spirit of the Lord has shown me you have much to teach me. I am your servant and your student."

Procorus invited Thoros and me to stay at his home. Throughout the week, many of the men who had listened to me in the synagogue came to ask questions and hear more about Jesus. Each time the crowd grew larger. But unlike what Thoros and I had witnessed in Hierapolis, many in the crowd were resisting the Spirit's invitation to become followers of Jesus. They were not hostile toward us, but neither were they accepting of the Gospel.

On the following Sabbath, Procorus, Thoros, and I went to the synagogue. A cluster of men was speaking in hushed tones to the rabbi. I recognized some of them from our meetings throughout the week. They looked at us warily, and I sensed we were the topic of conversation.

As we approached, the rabbi called out. "Saul, I understand you have been very active this week telling the people of our city about this One you say was the promised Savior of Israel. But I also understand you are saying this Man Jesus is also the Savior of the Gentiles – like this young man who is with you today – this one called Thoros. Is that correct?"

"Yes," I answered, "Jesus came for Jew and Gentile alike that their eyes might be opened, and they might *turn from darkness to light, and from the power of Satan to God. Then will they receive forgiveness for their sins and be given a place among God's people, who are set apart by faith in* Him."[5]

Immediately the rabbi and others gathered around him shouted, "Away with such a fellow! How dare he speak such blasphemy. We know that only we Jews are the chosen people of God! A Gentile must become a Jew if he seeks to be a child of God. Only by following the laws of Moses can sins be forgiven! Our leaders had this Jesus crucified because of the blasphemy He taught, and now this man teaches those same words! You are not welcome in this place!"

The rabbi and some of the other men tore their garments and began to cry out. Almost as if on cue, soldiers appeared to arrest us. The rabbi turned to the commander and shouted, "Arrest these men! They are creating a stir among the people by turning their hearts away from the one true God. They are inciting people with the lies of the Man Jesus whom you Romans crucified for His rebellious teachings." This had obviously been planned well in advance of our arrival that morning. The soldiers immediately bound our hands and led us away.

The commander never questioned us or tried to confirm the charges against us. When we arrived at the fortress, he instructed his soldiers to give me a scourging until I confessed my crimes. I was grateful when I realized Thoros and Procorus would not receive the same punishment. It was all being directed toward me.

I turned to the commander and asked, "Is it legal for you to whip a Roman citizen who hasn't even been tried?" But he acted like he never heard a word and directed his men to carry out his orders.

The powers of darkness were obviously at work here. I knew what was about to take place. As they stripped off my clothes, I heard one of the soldiers gasp. He could see I had endured this punishment several times before. As their whips began to tear at my flesh, I asked God to keep

Procorus and Thoros from harm. Soon after that, my Lord graciously permitted me to fall unconscious, as He had before, so I could escape the pain. My Lord knew all too well what this punishment felt like.

It was two days before I woke up to find Procorus and Thoros tending to the lacerations on my body. Procorus told me the commander said we would be released as soon as I was strong enough to walk. All three of us were then to leave the city immediately; if we failed to do so, we would be stoned to death. There would be no trial. We were to leave without speaking to anyone and never return.

I was in so much pain I would have been more than happy for Jesus to take me home to heaven. But I knew He had more for me to do. I also knew I would heal, and He would give me the strength. And He did just that until I was strong enough to leave.

As we had arranged, Thoros immediately departed for his home in Hierapolis. I had kept him away far too long. He needed to return and share all he had seen and heard, and to challenge the church to be faithful followers of Jesus.

Procorus and I made our way to the docks. I knew for now we needed to leave Cilicia. There was a ship preparing to set sail for Cyprus, and I knew Jesus wanted us to be on it. Within a matter of hours, the city of Seleucia began to fade into the distance as we sailed away from its shores.

* * *

15

Five different times the Jewish leaders gave me thirty-nine lashes. ...Three times I was shipwrecked. ... I have faced danger in the cities, in the deserts, and on the seas. ... I have worked hard and long, enduring many sleepless nights. I have been hungry and thirsty and have often gone without food.[1]

* * *

The sea was calm, and the winds were favorable as we began our three-day journey to Salamis. After our abrupt departure from Seleucia, I was grateful to the Lord for a few days of sea air and open spaces as we made our way to the eastern shore of Cyprus.

The ship sailed under a Cypriot flag, and we soon learned the captain and his small crew had set sail from Salamis six weeks earlier. They had carried Cypriot copper to Alexandria where they had exchanged it for Egyptian papyrus. From there, they had set sail for Athens where they exchanged a large portion of the papyrus for Athenian marble before departing for Seleucia. In Seleucia they had traded a portion of the marble for Cilician wheat and barley. They were now headed home laden with the rewards of their efforts: papyrus, marble, wheat, and barley. Cyprus relies heavily on imported goods through the efforts of merchant sailors like these men.

. . .

I learned that our captain, Andri, had not grown up on the sea; rather, his father had been a tentmaker. The captain grew up assisting in their family trade until he was old enough to leave home and pursue his own aspirations as a sailor. I told him I also had grown up as an apprentice tentmaker under my father, but now my life had taken a different course. When he asked the reason for my change of direction, I told him about my encounter with Jesus on the road to Damascus.

"*I was on the road, approaching Damascus about noon,*" *I said,* "*when a very bright light from heaven suddenly shone down around me. I fell to the ground and heard a voice speak to me* using my Hebrew name, *'Saul, Saul, why are you persecuting Me?'*[2]

"I asked Him who He was, and He replied, *'I am Jesus the Nazarene, the One you are persecuting.' The people with me saw the light but didn't understand the voice speaking to me.*[3]

"I asked, *'What should I do, Lord?'*[4]

"And He told me, *'Get up and go into Damascus, and there you will be told everything you are to do.'*[5]

"It was there He told me He had chosen me to be His witness, telling everyone what I had seen and heard."[6]

Our conversations about Jesus became a daily occurrence after that. I told him, as well as those who sailed with Him, all about Jesus – who He was, why He had come to earth, and what He had done for them on the cross. Soon, Andri and all his crew surrendered their lives to Jesus.

. . .

A terrible storm swept over us about a day away from our destination. It reminded me of the storm I experienced on the east side of Cyprus five years earlier. The sea and the winds became ominous. Procorus and I assisted the crew as Andri directed us to throw the marble overboard to lighten the ship. Soon he told us to cast off all the remaining goods in the hold of the ship. There would be no profit from this voyage – but prayerfully we would make it to shore.

I told Andri I was confident God would protect us through the storm. I knew He still had much more for me to do. As a matter of fact, the Spirit of God assured me we would all arrive on shore safely. Andri and the crew heard me, but at that moment they still had doubts.

We battled the storm throughout the night. The next morning, Andri set our course for a coastline that was visible in the distance. He did not recognize the area, but he knew we needed to find safe harbor from the unceasing storm.

As we approached the coastline, we hit a shoal and ran aground. Andri directed the crew to lower the lifeboat and abandon ship. After a great deal of effort, we finally made it to land and found shelter. Gratefully, by nightfall the storm had passed.

Andri was pleased to discover the ship's damage was minimal. He and the crew were able to make the needed repairs to the keel, and we made ready to continue our trip on to Salamis. Before we departed, I asked Andri if we could stop and thank God for His protection, His goodness, and His faithfulness to us. After we offered our praise and thanksgiving, I asked Andri if Procorus could baptize him and his crew there along the shore before we departed.

The men never hesitated. They took great joy in declaring their faith in Jesus. As we reboarded the ship, I wondered if God had allowed the storm so they might be baptized before they arrived home. I don't know the answer to that question, but I do know these men returned to their homes and their families transformed by the saving grace of Jesus.

Andri graciously invited Procorus and me to stay with his family. There was no question that our Lord had directed us to him. He was the person of peace God was always faithful to provide. He was that one Jesus had taught would open their home and extend hospitality for those whom He had sent out to proclaim the Gospel. His embracing welcome quickly opened the doors and hearts of his surrounding neighbors and the townspeople of Salamis.

As we preached the Gospel, we saw the Spirit of God draw many to faith in Jesus, including Andri's father and his older brother, Tomys – the tentmakers. As a matter of fact, it was obvious the Spirit was raising up Tomys to become the leader of this new church.

As the weeks passed, my physical strength began to return after being flogged, imprisoned, and even shipwrecked – and my spirit was encouraged. A growing and vibrant church had been born and was already beginning to multiply. Each time Andri returned from a voyage on the sea, he said he could see a difference in his town. Not only were individual lives being transformed but so was the town! The new believers were living lives filled with love for others. They were following the example of Christ Himself and had become a sweet perfume to Him.

I knew it was time for me to return to Tarsus; my work in Salamis was done. Andri arranged passage for Procorus and me to sail to Tarsus. The dock was filled with our new brothers and sisters in Christ to see us off. It was a sharp contrast to the stark scene in Seleucia when we had set sail for Salamis. At that moment, the Spirit reminded me my job was to plant the seeds of the Gospel no matter what –and to trust God for the increase. There would be days, like this day, when He would enable me to see the harvest. But there would be other days – like in Seleucia – when all I would witness was a Roman whip. He reminded me I was to continue to trust Him no matter the outcome.

. . .

Procorus knew he needed to return to Seleucia. So, when we arrived in Tarsus, I told him goodbye and he set off to find a ship on which to continue his journey, and I made my way to my family's home.

It had been four years since I had last seen them. My nephew Hezron met me at the door; I barely recognized him. He was now a head taller than I, and, at the age of thirteen, had become a young man. I wasn't aware just how much my appearance had changed – thanks to the years and the many difficulties I had endured – until I realized he did not recognize me.

"Hezron," I said. "It's your uncle Saul!"

He looked at me closer, and soon a faint look of recognition began to appear. He stepped forward and threw his arms around me with such strength and vigor my feet came off the ground.

"Mama!" he cried out. "Come see! It's Uncle Saul!"

Dinah appeared from around the corner carrying a child in her arms. My niece, Rachel, was now almost two years old. Dinah and I embraced, and soon were joined by my niece Esther, who at age seven was looking very much like her mother. It was good to be home – and good to be with family. While we enjoyed the moment, Hezron went to get his father. I was overjoyed to see Reuben again.

Soon I was telling them about everything that had occurred during my time away. I told them about the many people I had met in my travels, the many who had come to faith in Jesus, and the churches that had been planted. After seeing the scars all over my body, Dinah and the others listened in horror as I described the scourgings, beatings, imprisonments, the shipwreck, and the thieves who had left me for dead.

. . .

I soon turned the conversation to what was happening among the believers in Tarsus. I rejoiced as they told me the church had continued to thrive while I was away. More and more Gentiles had received the Lord's message and had become believers. Where there had been one group gathering at the home of Arsakes when I left, there were now twelve groups gathering in homes throughout the city.

Sadly, Benjamin and the other leaders of the synagogue had been able to dissuade most of the Jews from following Jesus. As belief continued to spread among the Gentiles, Benjamin convinced the Jews that this "false teaching" had nothing to do with God's chosen people and their promised Messiah was still yet to come. The Jews accepted what they were told, so Benjamin and the others no longer felt threatened by the Gospel message. I wept for my people and their blind guides. I had once been blind as well, and I prayed their eyes would one day be opened.

The response of the Gentiles had silenced Ashmus and the other critics. The people of the city were witnessing the miracle of changed lives in those who had become followers of Jesus. And the light of the Gospel was dispelling the darkness of the teachings of Ashmus and the others.

During the next several weeks, I focused on teaching Arsakes, Reuben, Dinah, and the other leaders of the churches, as well as those I knew were being faithful to teach others.

"*When I first came to you, dear brothers and sisters, I didn't use lofty words and impressive wisdom to tell you God's secret plan,*" I said. "*For I decided that while I was with you, I would forget everything except Jesus Christ, the One who was crucified. My message and my preaching were very plain. Rather than using clever and persuasive speeches, I relied only on the power of the Holy Spirit. I did this so you would trust not in human wisdom but in the power of God.*[7]

. . .

"Now you have become mature believers, so I *speak with words of wisdom, but not the kind of wisdom that belongs to this world or to the rulers of this world, who are soon forgotten. No, the wisdom I speak of is the mystery of God – His plan that was previously hidden, even though He made it for our ultimate glory before the world began.*"[8]

I went on to explain that the mystery of God is the salvation of Jew *and* Gentile through the sacrifice of Jesus on the cross of Calvary – not through the law passed down from Moses. We have been saved through the amazing grace of God. And He has extended His salvation as a free gift. It is not a gift given through the eloquence of words but through the power of God.

I told them, "*God has now revealed to us His mysterious will regarding Christ – which is to fulfill His own good plan. And this is the plan: At the right time He will bring everything together under the authority of Christ – everything in heaven and on earth. Furthermore, because we are united with Christ, we have received an inheritance from God, for He chose us in advance, and He makes everything work out according to His plan.*[9]

"Work hard so you can present yourself to God and receive His approval. Be good workers who do not need to be ashamed and who correctly explain the word of truth. Avoid worthless, foolish talk that only leads to godless behavior. Because God's truth stands firm like a foundation stone. Run from anything that stimulates lust. Instead, pursue righteous living, faithfulness, love, and peace. Enjoy the companionship of those who call on the Lord with pure hearts. Do not quarrel but be kind to everyone, be faithful to teach, and be patient with difficult people. Gently instruct those who oppose the truth. Perhaps God will change those people's hearts, and they will learn the truth, come to their senses, and escape from the devil's trap."[10]

The weeks raced by as I witnessed the godly transition taking place in the lives of these men and women. There was a part of me that wanted to remain with them in Tarsus for the rest of my days. The city had truly become my home. It was no longer simply the place where I had been born and raised; it was now also the place where the Spirit of God had chosen to encourage me in the work and refresh me.

But one day, as I sat with the leaders teaching them these things, I saw a familiar face appear before me. He peered at me from the back of the crowd and smiled. I knew my life was again about to change.

* * *

16

Then Barnabas went on to Tarsus to look for Saul. When he found him, he brought him back to Antioch. Both of them stayed there with the church for a full year, teaching large crowds of people. (It was at Antioch that the believers were first called Christians.)[1]

* * *

"What are you doing here in Tarsus?" I asked my friend Barnabas. It had been seven years since I had last seen him in Caesarea Maritima. I knew he had returned to Jerusalem at the time to continue his work among the believers there.

"The Spirit of God is moving upon the Gentiles in the city of Antioch in Syria, and a large number have believed and turned to the Lord," he replied. "When the church in Jerusalem heard what was happening, James sent me to Antioch to investigate the reports. When I arrived there and saw the proof of God's favor, I was overjoyed.

"I began to assist the believers to encourage them and train them up in their understanding of the Scriptures. But I knew I needed help – and the

Spirit of the Lord came to me in a vision and prompted me to find you and bring you back to work alongside me.

"A few days earlier, I had met a physician by the name of Luke. He told me he had become a follower of Jesus through your teaching here in Tarsus and that the Spirit of God was moving here. He said he last saw you in Aegeae, so I immediately headed there.

"When I arrived in Aegeae, I talked to my good friend Timon. He told me how he had traveled with you to Anazarbus and how the Lord had used you in those cities. He said he recently received word you were back here in Tarsus encouraging believers. So, I have come to ask you to join me in the work in Antioch, for there is much to be done."

As soon as Barnabas spoke those words, the Holy Spirit affirmed that I was to go with him without delay. I said goodbye to my family and friends, and two days later we began our journey. It took us three days to reach Aegeae by foot. We spent the evening with Timon and the other brothers. We rejoiced in the news of all that God was doing among them.

Marius reported that the commander of the fortress had recently become a follower of Jesus. Though the Jews were continuing to resist the Good News, Gentiles were coming to faith in large numbers. God was truly doing a tremendous work among them. I challenged the leaders to seek the Lord regarding sending out some of their mature brothers and sisters to go into Cappadocia and proclaim the Good News to those there who had yet to hear it.

The next morning Barnabas and I booked passage on the ferry to cross the bay. Five days later we arrived in Antioch, the capital of Syria, located 480 kilometers north of Jerusalem. It boasts a population of half a million people, which currently makes it the third largest city in the Roman Empire, surpassed only by Rome and Alexandria. Because it is a busy port city and a center for luxury and culture, it attracts all kinds of people, including wealthy retired Roman officials who spend their days conversing in the baths or gambling at the chariot races.

With Antioch's large cosmopolitan population and its great commercial and political power, the people living there want for very little. It is also a wicked city, perhaps eclipsed only by Corinth. Though all the Syrian, Greek, and Roman deities are honored in the city, the principal shrine is dedicated to Daphne, whose worship includes immoral rituals. More than any other city I have visited, it is a city filled with every possible epicurean temptation.

One of the first people we met was Luke, who greeted us warmly. "I prayed you would find him," Luke said, nodding at Barnabas. Then he turned to me and continued, "I knew the day we parted ways in Aegeae that God would permit me to see you again. And now by His grace, He has brought you to us at a time when you are so greatly needed."

Luke led us to his home and introduced me to his father and mother. They had settled in Antioch many years earlier before Luke was born. Luke's father had been an affluent physician trained under some of the finest physicians in Athens. Luke's parents always expected him to follow in his father's footsteps. And that is exactly what he had done. He went to Athens to be trained and then returned to Antioch to establish his own medical practice. He had successfully – and very satisfactorily – practiced medicine for twenty years and had a very comfortable life.

That is until the day our paths crossed. He told me that since then, God had been stirring his heart to say goodbye to the comforts of his prosperous medical practice. Instead, he believed he was to travel on a mission with much greater purpose. He told me he wasn't clear on what that would be, but he knew God had brought me to Antioch to help him discover what it was.

. . .

His parents had also become followers of Jesus after they saw the change that had taken place in their son's life. Though they didn't completely agree with his decision to stop practicing medicine, they trusted their son and knew he was following God's direction. Luke and his parents invited Barnabas and me to stay with them. We welcomed the opportunity to help nurture them and prepare them for the decisions they would likely need to make in the days ahead.

Since his return to Antioch, Luke had been of great assistance to Simeon, Lucius, and Manaen, the principal leaders and elders of the church there. How different these men were! The next morning, Luke and Barnabas took me to meet them.

I listened intently as Simeon told me his story. He is a dark-skinned Gentile, originally from southern Nubia on the continent of Africa. He grew up in the capital city of Medewi, whose culture was greatly shaped by years of Egyptian influence and the more recent effects of Greek culture on the entire region. As such, Simeon spoke three languages – Coptic, Greek, and his native Meroitic.

Simeon's family had accumulated their wealth through their success in metalworking. His family, and others in that region, were profiting from the export of iron along the Silk Road into China. In fact, his family had supplied much of the iron used by Herod Antipas in the construction of his beloved capital city, Tiberias. It was a business trip from Medewi to Tiberias related to that work that ultimately led him to an encounter with Jesus.

"As I was approaching Jericho on my way to Tiberias," Simeon explained, "I met a teacher with a large following leaving the city. I was passing by the crowd when I saw a blind beggar sitting by the side of the road. The beggar was shouting at the teacher, '*Jesus, Son of David, have mercy on me!*'(2)

"I heard Jesus ask him, '*What do you want me to do for you?*'(3)

. . .

"*'Rabbi,'* the blind man replied, *'I want to see!'*[4]

"I was amazed when Jesus answered him and said, *'Go, for your faith has healed you.'*[5] Jesus had simply spoken those words, and in a moment the man jumped to his feet and immediately proclaimed he could see. I soon learned the man had been blind since birth.

"I marveled at what I had witnessed, so I decided to follow Jesus and learn more about Him. I noticed the blind man was doing the same. Even though Jesus and the crowd were heading in the opposite direction of my journey, I knew I needed to turn and follow. They led me to Jerusalem on the day that would prove to be His triumphal entry into the city.

"I watched with awe as the crowd praised Jesus that day. I listened closely as He taught in the temple. Then, later in the week, I watched in horror when they nailed Him to the cross. By then, I knew He was the Son of God. I had already made the decision to follow Him – but my faith was shaken for those three days His body lay in the tomb. By His grace, I was one of the people who saw Jesus over the next several weeks after He rose from the dead. I stood on the mount the day He ascended into heaven. I sat in the upper room, when the building shook, and the Spirit of Christ descended upon us!

"My mission changed that day. I traveled to Tiberias to complete my family's errand. That was the day I met Manaen. A few days later, the two of us traveled back to Jerusalem where we remained until the Holy Spirit directed us to come to Antioch."

By the time he was done telling his story, he was weeping and praising God saying, "By God's grace He saved me. By His grace He chose me and gave me the honor of telling others about His Good News!"

. . .

Manaen shared next. "When Herod the Great attained the summit of his power, he sought the counsel of an Essene he had known as a boy. Herod knew this man to be of sound wisdom, and the man served him well. An unlikely friendship developed between them. Herod chose to reward the Essene by offering to be the patron of the man's grandson – I am that grandson.

"It was quite an adjustment for me to leave the stern purity of the life of the Essenes and enter into the pomp and luxury of Herod's court to be raised as the foster brother of two of Herod's sons – Antipas and Archelaus. It was an even greater change when all three of us were sent to Rome to further our educations.

"After my studies were completed, I returned to the palace, now fully accustomed to a royal lifestyle. The bond between me and my foster brother Antipas was strong. I truly loved him like a brother. When Herod the Great died, I remained with Antipas as he became the client king over Galilee and Perea.

"I turned a blind eye to Antipas's incestuous marriage to Herodias, but the teachings of John the baptizer were influencing me. As time went on, several in the court of Antipas became disciples of John, and soon others became disciples of Jesus. The witness of these new disciples made a big impact on me, as it did on others in the palace. The imprisonment of John brought him into closer contact with many of us in the household because Antipas often called for John and liked to listen to him speak.

"The turning point in my life came when Antipas gave orders for John to be beheaded. I knew that Chuza, Antipas's household manager, was a follower of Jesus as was his wife, Joanna. Jesus had healed their son when he lay at death's door. And Joanna was now frequently traveling with Jesus and His many followers. Through the witness of John, Chuza, and Joanna, I became a secret follower of Jesus.

. . .

"Then came the news that Jesus had been crucified – and Antipas had played a role in His death. I asked God to show me what He would have me do. A few weeks later, I met Simeon. When he told me his story and what he had witnessed, I knew I must leave the palace in Tiberias and go to Jerusalem with him. I've never looked back.

"Simeon and I both come from wealthy backgrounds, materially. But we would tell you that our wealth is not measured by money or possessions; our true wealth is measured by God's overflowing grace in our lives. We know He has placed us here to proclaim His Good News and lead this fellowship of believers who many are now calling 'Christians.' We will use every breath we possess, every coin in our treasury, and every bit of our influence for the sake of the Gospel."

Lucius was a Jew from Cyrene. "I was in Jerusalem for the observance of Passover, just as I had been many times before," he said. "I was there when they crucified Jesus, but I was not a follower. I was like many who stood in the crowd, blindly following our religious leaders. They told us He was a heretic and an insurrectionist. Who were we to question them? They were our leaders. They knew best – or so we thought!

"But as I watched the soldiers leading Jesus to the cross, I saw that another man was carrying His cross. As I looked closer, I realized it was my cousin Simon. The soldiers had apparently pulled him out of the crowd to carry the cross. I saw a Roman whip strike my cousin's back. Suddenly, this crucifixion became very personal to me!

"I followed at a distance. After they raised Jesus on the cross, I saw Simon kneeling there – at the foot of the cross. He wasn't trying to get away. The crowd and the soldiers seemed out of control. I was afraid to walk up and stand with my cousin. I wanted to remain a 'safe' distance away, hidden in the crowd. But I watched Jesus's anguish on the cross. I stood in the darkness that overtook us in the middle of the day. I heard Jesus when He gasped, *'It is finished!'*[(6)]

. . .

"I continued to watch as my cousin carried the lifeless body of Jesus to the place where He was to be buried. Only after His body had been placed in the tomb did I approach my cousin. As Simon explained everything that had happened and what he had seen, he added, 'Jesus truly was the Son of the Living God. He was the One whose coming was foretold. I do not know how, but I know He will rise again. Because death has no power over the Son of the Living God!'

"I was amazed as my cousin confessed his faith. But I am ashamed to admit I did not believe in Jesus until after He had risen from the dead. Simon sought me out to tell me! He was in the upper room the night Jesus appeared to His disciples. When he told me Jesus was alive, I could not help but believe. Everything within me told me it was true – He was who He said He was. That night I became a follower of Jesus!

"A few weeks later I was there on the mount when Jesus went up to heaven. I met Simeon and Manaen that day as well. Our friendship blossomed and we began serving together. God brought us together from three very different places, different languages, and different backgrounds. But He brought us together at the foot of the cross for one purpose – to serve Him on bended knee and with willing hearts ... no matter where He leads."

They had come to Antioch armed with the Word of God on their lips and the Spirit of God in their hearts. As a result of their boldness and confidence in the Spirit, a number of Gentiles believed and turned to the Lord.

The leaders of the church in Jerusalem had sent someone gifted as an encourager – Barnabas – to come alongside them. He was not sent to "take charge" of the mission but rather to strengthen a Spirit-led movement. Through his encouragement, these three men and this thriving church had continued to grow and multiply. He recognized there was now need for another shepherd to nurture and disciple this growing body.

• • •

Barnabas could have easily sent word back to James and the other elders in Jerusalem requesting they send someone to assist him. But Barnabas knew God had commissioned me to minister to the Gentiles, so he made the effort to seek me out. God had used Barnabas to encourage and pour into my life in Jerusalem; now he would do the same as we would co-labor in Antioch.

That evening I thought about what these three men had told me. I thanked God for the opportunity to be in Antioch with them and with Barnabas during God's overwhelming activity.

We never know how God will use the experiences and relationships in our lives to further His purpose and plan. We must think of ourselves as an arrow being sent by the bow in the hands of the Master Archer. His aim is true. He always hits His target. He has shaped each one of us uniquely as arrows, fittingly suited for the path and the target He has chosen. We may have been shaped very differently by the experiences in our lives. We may come from different backgrounds, different ethnicities, different languages, and different races. But we have all been crafted as an "arrow" for His purpose. We have all been sent! None of us has been crafted to remain in the quiver!

17

So the believers in Antioch decided to send relief to the brothers and sisters in Judea, everyone giving as much as they could.[(1)]

* * *

I knew the religious beliefs of the Gentiles in Antioch originally centered around the gods of their Greek ancestors. But over the years, the continuing flow of other cultures into Antioch brought scores of other religious beliefs, including those with doctrines of salvation, of death and regeneration, and promises of an afterlife. Most of the citizens of Antioch – except the Jews – prided themselves on their acceptance of a diversity of religious beliefs. That atmosphere of religious tolerance had been promoted and protected by the city's Roman leaders since the beginning of their rule.

Soon after I arrived in Antioch, Luke arranged for me to meet the governor – a man named Theophilus. He and Luke had been friends since childhood. Theophilus had witnessed the change in Luke's life since he had become a follower of Jesus, but Theophilus was still reluctant to surrender his own life. Luke asked if I would meet with him and answer any lingering questions he had, and I said I would.

. . .

Theophilus's father, Valerian, had been a trusted member of the Roman senate early in the reign of Emperor Tiberius. In recognition of his loyalty and achievements, the emperor had appointed him to the role of governor and dispatched him from Rome to Antioch in 14 A.D. His official title was "envoy of the emperor," and it was a tremendous personal honor because Antioch was a coveted appointment.

Theophilus was just a lad when the family arrived in Antioch. It was soon after that he and Luke were introduced. They were about the same age and soon became fast friends.

Governor Valerian was popular with the citizens of Antioch, and the city thrived under his leadership. The emperor and senate were pleased with his performance, so they allowed him to serve in that capacity for an unprecedented twenty-seven years.

When the time came for Valerian to step down, he recommended to Emperor Claudius that Theophilus be considered for the appointment. The emperor agreed, and Theophilus assumed the position as the new governor of Antioch. The citizens of the city were overjoyed with the decision. They considered him to be one of their own since they had watched him grow up. They were confident he would be a fair and capable leader just like his father – and he was.

Theophilus was gracious and cordial as he welcomed Luke and me into his home. I could quickly see why these two had become such good friends. Their personalities were very similar. Our conversations were easy and unguarded. Theophilus wasted no time, however, directing the conversation to the questions he wanted to discuss.

"Paul, I understand you were trained as a Jewish rabbi," he said. "As such, I am speaking with you as the learned teacher you are. Tell me, how is it that you believe Jesus of Nazareth was truly the Son of God – and the only Son of God at that?"

I responded, "*The God of the nation of Israel chose our ancestors and made them multiply and grow strong during their stay in Egypt. Then with a powerful arm He led them out of their slavery. He put up with them through forty years of wandering in the wilderness. Then He destroyed seven nations in Canaan and gave their land to Israel as an inheritance. All this took about four hundred fifty years.*

"*After that, God gave them judges to rule until the time of Samuel the prophet. Then the people begged for a king, and God gave them Saul, son of Kish, a man of the tribe of Benjamin, who reigned for forty years. But God removed Saul and replaced him with David, a man about whom God said, 'I have found David, son of Jesse, a man after my own heart. He will do everything I want him to do.'*

"*And it is one of King David's descendants, Jesus, who is God's promised Savior of Israel! Before He came, John the baptizer preached that all the people of Israel needed to repent of their sins and turn to God and be baptized. As John was finishing his ministry he asked, 'Do you think I am the Messiah? No, I am not! But He is coming soon – and I'm not even worthy to be His slave and untie the sandals on His feet.'*

"*This message of salvation has been sent to the sons of Abraham as well as God-fearing Gentiles! The people in Jerusalem and their leaders did not recognize Jesus as the one the prophets had spoken about. Instead, they condemned Him, and in doing this they fulfilled the prophets' words that are read every Sabbath by the Jews. They found no legal reason to execute Him, but they asked Pilate to have Him killed anyway.*

"*When they had done all that the prophecies said about Him, they took Him down from the cross and placed Him in a tomb. But God raised Him from the dead*[2] *on the third day, just as the Scriptures said. He was seen by His apostle, Peter, and then by the Twelve. After that, He was seen by more than five hundred of His followers at one time, most of whom are still alive, though some have died. Last of all, as though I had been born at the wrong time, I also saw Him. For I am the least of all the apostles. In fact, I'm not even worthy to be called an apostle after the way I persecuted God's church.*[3]

"I stand before you as one who has seen Him. He alone has conquered death. Though He was dead, yet He lives! He alone is the resurrection and the life. The one true God – the Creator of all things – sent His only Son as the Lamb of God to take away the sins of the world – including my sins and your sins, Governor Theophilus."

Theophilus became a follower of Jesus that day and, in so doing, became part of the church in Antioch. In the days ahead, he became a selfless leader of the church, a protector of the church (in his role as governor), and a great benefactor. Together with Manaen and Simeon, he financially supported my efforts in making the Gospel known among the Gentiles.

Barnabas and I continued teaching the growing number of believers there for the next year. Toward the end of that year, a group of prophets arrived from Jerusalem. Their chief spokesman was a man named Agabus. He stood up in one of the meetings, clearly empowered by the Spirit of God, and predicted a great famine would soon come upon the entire Roman world.

I watched as the believers began to react to this news. Their concern was not for themselves; instead, they worried how they could assist their persecuted brothers and sisters in Judea through this disaster. They took up an offering because they knew that to whom much has been given, much is required. They knew the Gospel had been given to them at a great cost – the shed blood of Jesus – and the shed blood of the Jerusalem martyrs. And they knew whatever they gave would pale in comparison to the price the Judean believers had paid for them – so everyone gave as much as they could.

. . .

They chose to send their gifts to Jerusalem through Barnabas and me. It would give us a chance to report to the elders about what the Spirit was doing among the Gentiles – particularly in Antioch. But I couldn't help but think about the irony: here I was delivering relief back to the very church I had persecuted! We set out on our journey so we would arrive in Jerusalem in time for the observance of Passover.

When we arrived, we went directly to Mnason's home. My joy at reuniting with my friend was somewhat overshadowed by his news. He told us how the church was in an uproar. In the eight years that had passed since I was last in Jerusalem, the political landscape had changed dramatically. Herod Antipas, whose political standing had been weakened by his defeat by Nabatean King Aretas, fell out of favor with Emperor Caligula. He was sent into exile in Spain, and his nephew (Agrippa I) had quickly risen as the new favored son of Rome. The emperor decided to recall the Roman prefect from Judea and reunite the kingdom, which had been split after the death of Agrippa's grandfather, Herod the Great. Agrippa was appointed governor over the entire region of Judea, Samaria, Galilee, and Perea – and carried the title of king.

After the crucifixion of Jesus, the Roman prefect had somewhat protected the apostles and elders of the Jerusalem church from retribution by the Jewish leaders. Though the official had turned a blind eye to the stoning of Stephen and Parmenas, it had been clear that no one was permitted to harm Peter, James, or the other apostles and elders. When the Roman prefect was recalled to Rome and Agrippa was appointed governor, that protection no longer existed.

As a matter of fact, King Agrippa desired to curry favor with the Jewish leaders – and what better way to do so than persecute some of the church leaders. Apparently, the Jewish leaders had made their wishes known to Agrippa. Mnason told us that one week before our arrival in Jerusalem, the apostle James (the son of Zebedee) had been arrested.

• • •

We asked the church elders if they knew why James had been jailed. They said it was because the Jewish leaders knew Peter, John, and James had been the closest of the apostles to Jesus. Those three men had been with Him on several occasions when the rest of the apostles were not. John, as I well knew, had a unique familial relationship with the Jewish leaders. He was the great-grand-nephew of Hillel the Elder and had briefly been a talmid of Rabbi Gamaliel. Given those connections, they had no interest in having him arrested. Peter was obviously the main spokesman, but they feared how the people would react to his arrest. Though James was also related to Hillel, he had never walked in those circles. So, they had chosen James.

Agrippa made the decision to have James killed with a sword. When he saw how much this pleased the Jewish leaders, it emboldened him to have Peter arrested – which occurred on the very day we arrived in Jerusalem. We heard that Agrippa planned to deal with Peter in a much more public way than he had with James. Instead of simply putting him to death, Peter would be placed on trial for the false charges being brought against him.

Throughout the Passover, Barnabas and I gathered with Mnason and the other believers to pray for Peter's release. The night before Peter was to be tried, many of us gathered in the home of Mary. She was an aunt of Barnabas and Mnason. Barnabas had brought her to meet Jesus soon after he believed, and she had become a devout follower as had her son, John Mark.

After we had been praying for a while, Mary's servant, Rhoda, entered the room and told us, *"Peter is standing at the door!"*(4)

"You're out of your mind!"(5) someone said.

But Rhoda insisted, so we all followed her to the door. To our amazement, there stood Peter! He motioned for us to quiet down as he explained that an angel had delivered him from his cell and had led him out of prison. Before he departed, he instructed us to tell James (the half brother of Jesus) and the other elders what had happened.

The next morning word traveled quickly through the streets that Peter had disappeared. Agrippa's soldiers had searched through the night to no avail. Those who were guarding Peter were put to death. Agrippa was livid; he hastily left Jerusalem to escape the humiliation of being bested by a Galilean fisherman. We all knew it hadn't been a Galilean fisherman who bested him, it was a Galilean Carpenter!

As the news of Peter's escape spread, so did the Good News! And there were many new believers as a result.

The morning after Peter's escape, Mary approached Barnabas and me about taking her son, John Mark, with us when we returned to Antioch. "Since his father died," she said, "he has not had the influence of mature godly men in his life. Try as I might, I have not been able to help him find men here in Jerusalem who will invest themselves in his life. Those I would trust to do so are consumed with the responsibilities of nurturing a growing multitude of new believers. And those who do have the time, do not possess a spiritual maturity they can pass along.

"Barnabas, you are my oldest sister's son. In many ways, you are my father in the faith having led me to Jesus. John Mark looks up to you as if you were his older, wiser uncle. Saul, I see John Mark sit with rapt attention as he listens to every word you speak. Please take him with you and nurture him in the ways of the Lord!"

We agreed to do so, though I was somewhat reluctant. I was not certain he had the stamina and commitment necessary to do what we needed to do. But Barnabas had taken a chance on me when no one else would. How could I do any less for John Mark?

. . .

Two days later, we received news that an earthquake had occurred in Antioch. We had no idea what devastation we would find, but we knew we must get there quickly.

* * *

18

One day as these men were worshiping the Lord and fasting, the Holy Spirit said, "Appoint Barnabas and Saul for the special work to which I have called them."[1]

* * *

It had been ten years since the last earthquake shook Antioch; Tiberius was emperor at the time. As we neared our destination, we learned that shockwaves from this last quake had triggered a tsunami damaging harbors and ports as far away as Caesarea Maritima. But nothing could have prepared us for the destruction and death we saw when Barnabas, John Mark, and I arrived.

Witnesses told us the earthquake began with a loud roar and then the ground shook violently. Whole trees, along with people, were thrown into the air. Numerous residents were killed by falling debris from collapsing buildings. The aftershocks continued for several days, killing many who were still trapped in the rubble. Others died of starvation and dehydration before they could be rescued.

. . .

Theophilus's son and daughter, as well as several believers and their children, were among those who died. Luke's parents were trapped in their home a few days before eventually being rescued. Two of the believers, Rufus and Aurelius, were killed by falling debris while attempting to rescue others. Lucius and Manaen were both injured by collapsing buildings, but their injuries were not fatal.

Even during his grief, Theophilus mobilized soldiers stationed in Antioch to lead the search and rescue efforts. He had Simeon mobilize the church to also provide aid – food, shelter, and clothing – to those who had been most severely impacted by the quake. The church responded quickly and selflessly.

By the time we arrived, most every church family whose home had not been destroyed or severely damaged was providing shelter to at least one displaced family. It wasn't long before the community noticed it was the Christians, as believers were now being called, who were providing the greatest assistance. They began asking why the believers would help total strangers so selflessly. As a result, many folks heard the Gospel and came to faith in Jesus.

Barnabas, John Mark, and I rolled up our sleeves to help our brothers and sisters in ministering to the needs of the city by day. Then at night, we met with the growing number of new believers – discipling them in their newfound faith in Jesus. Lucius and Manaen soon recovered from their injuries and joined us in the effort as well.

Luke proved to be a remarkable instrument of God's mercy and grace as he labored tirelessly as a physician. Temporary facilities were set up across the city to provide treatment for the injured. In most instances, those helping Luke provide care were also believers. But Luke's care wasn't limited to the physical needs; he also compassionately ministered to the many emotional needs. I watched as he compassionately walked with Theophilus through his grief.

. . .

I believe the earthquake was a turning point in the life of the church of Antioch. The believers transitioned from simply being silent followers of Jesus to becoming His hands and feet. They loved the people in their city with the love of Jesus – and the city saw it and responded!

As weeks turned into months and we were no longer in a crisis, I saw their relationship with Christ deepen and mature. They knew God was leading them to follow Him in even more meaningful ways.

Barnabas, Simeon, Lucius, Manaen, and I fasted and prayed as we sought God's guidance about the next step He was leading the church to take. We knew it was a crucial step, but we didn't know what or how monumental that step would be. God was about to use this church to impact the world.

One day as we were worshiping and fasting, the Holy Spirit said to us, *"Appoint Barnabas and Saul for the special work to which I have called them."*[(2)] I knew Jesus had called me and prepared me to take His message to the Gentiles. Barnabas also knew God had been preparing him to join me and do the same. But this was now also a call on the church. The Holy Spirit was telling them they were to send us out. They were to support us with their prayers. They were to send out other members to assist us in the work as needed. And they were to support us financially. God was not only calling Barnabas and me to go; He was also calling the church to go with us through their support.

That evening we told the church what the Holy Spirit said. God had called us and anointed us; the church was now to send us out. There were mixed emotions as the church processed everything. They were sad we were leaving but excited about what God was going to do through our obedience. They already knew what the Spirit of God had done in their midst. They had seen the Gospel message come to their city. They had experienced a life change through the power of the Gospel. They had witnessed the change that had taken place in their city. They knew the power of the Gospel!

• • •

And now they were being invited by God to join in the task of carrying the Gospel around the world where it had never been heard. They knew that sending us out was not bidding us farewell, rather they would be "going" with us. God would reward this step of faithfulness and they would be used by God to help carry His message to the rest of the world. As the magnitude of this gripped their hearts, they began praising God. Their worship continued throughout the night and into the next day. Barnabas and I knew the time had come for us to go. The elders who would remain – Simeon, Lucius, and Manaen – laid hands on us and led the church in praying for us. The next day, they sent us on our way.

Barnabas and I discussed what we should do with John Mark. Should he stay in Antioch, return to Jerusalem, or go with us? His mother had entrusted him into our care for us to nurture him. As we sought the Lord's guidance, it became clear that John Mark was to accompany us. So, the three of us set out on the journey together.

We felt the Lord leading us to first preach the Gospel across the island of Cyprus, so we departed on a ship bound for Salamis. It was a two-day journey on smooth seas. The ship's captain, Andreas, was well acquainted with my friend, Andri. As a matter of fact, Andri had recently shared the Gospel with him, and Andreas had placed his faith in Jesus. Throughout our short voyage, Barnabas and I both had the opportunity to teach him – as well as his crew – more about Jesus. By the time we docked in Salamis, all the crew had come to believe!

Tomys greeted us when we arrived at Andri's home. Andri and his crew had departed just two days prior on a trading voyage and were not expected to return for several weeks. But Tomys and the rest of the family welcomed us with open arms and told us there would always be room for us to stay with them.

We were overjoyed to hear how many new Gentile believers had been added to the church in Salamis. Tomys told us they were hungry to learn more but had many questions he could not answer. We decided to stay for a while so we could help him and the church grow in their understanding of God's Word. It would also give us an opportunity to go into the local Jewish synagogues and preach the Gospel – something which I had not been able to do on my previous visit.

Sadly, the people in the synagogues were not receptive to the Word of God. The men challenged us with questions but rejected our answers – unlike the Gentiles who responded to our answers with a hunger to hear more. Their thirst for the Word of God was undeniable. We soon sensed a release from the Spirit to concentrate on the Gentile believers in the town exclusively.

We had been in Salamis for about four weeks when we felt the Lord prompting us to move on. Tomys volunteered to travel with us, as did another believer named Hasan. We preached from town to town as we made our way to the western side of the island. As each day passed, it became even clearer how God had uniquely equipped Barnabas and me to complement one another on this mission. His encouraging nature put people at ease and created opportunities for me to present the Good News. My prophetic nature provoked Barnabas to an even greater understanding of the truths of God, which in turn enabled him to be a more effective encourager. God knew exactly what each of us needed, and He had certainly brought us together for His purpose.

Within days after our arrival in the capital city of Paphos, we received an invitation from Sergio Paulus, the proconsul (governor) of Cyprus. He had been told we were drawing crowds in the city as we taught about Jesus. Evidently, he wanted to hear the Word of God personally.

But when we arrived at his home, another man was with him. He was a funny-looking little man, even shorter than I am. He spoke with a shrill voice, and his head bobbed up and down when he spoke. He reminded me of one of those comical hand puppets used in Greek plays. But, there was nothing comical about him. He was introduced to us as Elymas, a Jewish sorcerer.

Barnabas and I quickly discerned he was a false prophet sent by Satan to keep the proconsul from accepting the truth of God. He had apparently gained influence over the proconsul in the past, and now – through his magic, his lies, and his interruptions – he was endeavoring to prevent us from sharing the Good News. He became so bold as to say, "Pay no attention to what these men are saying. This man Paul has been imprisoned on more than one occasion for spreading his lies."

Satan knows he is a defeated foe. But given the liar that he is, he had never told Elymas his efforts would ultimately fail. Thus, his false prophet, Elymas, was on the losing side of the battle. He may have appeared to be having a momentary victory, but it was short-lived. I looked the sorcerer in the eye and, filled with the Holy Spirit, I said, *"You son of the devil, full of every sort of deceit and fraud, and enemy of all that is good! Will you never stop perverting the true ways of the Lord? Watch now, for the Lord has laid His hand of punishment upon you, and you will be struck blind. You will not see the sunlight for some time."*(3)

Instantly a mist and darkness fell upon him, and he began to wander about pleading for someone to take his hand and guide him. But the greater act of the Spirit of God was that He opened the eyes of Sergius Paulus to the truth. When the proconsul saw what had happened, he immediately believed and asked that we teach him more about Jesus.

"I have heard stories about this Man, Jesus," he said. "But I thought they were just stories. Now I know the stories are true. He is the one true God, and from this day forth I will follow Him."

The proconsul called for all his household to come and listen to Barnabas and me. After we had shared the Good News with his family and his servants, they also believed in Jesus. The news of what happened to Elymas quickly spread throughout the city. A crowd began to assemble outside the proconsul's home as we stood on the roof and preached the Gospel. Before the day was over, Barnabas, Tomys, and I had baptized the proconsul, the members of his household, and a multitude of others throughout the city.

We remained in Paphos for two more weeks – preaching the Good News and discipling new believers. One night, the Spirit told me it was time for us to go to Antioch of Pisidia. The next morning, before Barnabas and I were able to tell Tomys of our plans, he came to us saying, "The Spirit of God has shown me you are to continue your travels, but Hasan and I are to remain here for a while to carry on the work He has begun through you. Once our work is completed, we will return to Salamis. But in the meantime, we must all do what God has clearly shown us to do."

The next day, Barnabas, John Mark, and I bid farewell to our many new brothers and sisters in Christ and boarded a trading ship setting sail for a three-day journey to the port town of Perga in Pamphylia. The captain told us Perga was the ship's first destination. From there they would sail on to Sidon, followed by Caesarea Maritima, and then return home to Paphos. John Mark perked up when the captain mentioned Caesarea Maritima. Barnabas and I tried to engage the captain in conversation, but we soon realized neither he nor his crew had any interest in hearing about God. We decided to spend the remainder of our time on the ship in extended prayer.

Later that day, John Mark approached me expressing a desire to return home to Jerusalem. He said he was concerned about his widowed mother and her care. I assured him the church in Jerusalem was being attentive to her needs. She was not lacking for people around her to encourage her and watch out for her.

But he persisted and asked me when I thought we would return. I told him the Spirit of God was leading us in our mission. We would trust His leadership and His time frame. I had no idea when we might return, but given the fact that we had only left Antioch less than two months earlier, I didn't expect it would be anytime soon. I reminded Him of the task God had given us to take the Gospel to those who had not heard. Even though many believers had departed from Jerusalem, there were still many who had remained there to tell others about Jesus. The people who lived in the places we were going had never heard His name. And in most of those places there was no one yet there to tell them.

Though he seemed to understand what I was saying, it did not appear to ease his anxiety. He stayed to himself for the remainder of our voyage, only speaking to Barnabas or me on occasion. I encouraged him to continue to lift up his mother to the Father in prayer. "He is her Heavenly Father," I said. "He knows best what she needs, and He is able to take care of her far better than you or anyone else can. Commit her to His care, and continue to run the race He has set before you." I could tell by his demeanor, though, that he continued to worry.

When we arrived in Perga, we located a place to stay and settled in for a good night's rest. The next morning, we discovered a note from John Mark. It read, "I am sorry to disappoint you both, but I have returned to the ship to join them on their continuing voyage to Caesarea Maritima. From there I will return to Jerusalem. I will pray that God grants you both favor as you carry on with the mission He has set before you."

Though we were both disappointed, neither Barnabas nor I was surprised. We returned to the docks to discover the ship had already set sail earlier that morning. We committed our young charge in prayer to the care of our Lord and trusted Him for his safe return home. We then turned our attention to setting out on our two-day journey on foot to Antioch of Pisidia.

The day after we arrived was the Sabbath, so we went to the synagogue. After the usual readings from the books of Moses and the prophets had been completed, the rabbi leading the service said to us, *"Brothers, if you have any word of encouragement for the people, come and give it."*[4]

• • •

I stood to my feet and said, *"Men of Israel and you God-fearing Gentiles, listen to me."*[(5)] I then proceeded to recount God's promise of a Savior from the days of the ancestors leading up to the advent of Jesus. *"Brothers,"* I said, *"listen! We are here to proclaim that through this man Jesus there is forgiveness for your sins. Everyone who believes in Him is made right in God's sight – something the law of Moses could never do."*[(6)]

After the service, a number of people came up to us and asked if we would return the following Sabbath so we could tell them more about these things. Several of the men told us they had believed. I urged them, *"By God's grace, remain faithful!"*[(7)]

Throughout the week, we continued to teach those who had believed and preached to those who would listen. By the following Sabbath, it appeared the entire city had turned out at the synagogue to hear us. There was not enough room inside for everyone, so we remained outside and began to teach them the Word of the Lord.

But when some of the Jewish leaders saw the size of the crowd, they became jealous and started slandering us and arguing against everything I said. They swayed most of the Jews in the crowd to reject the truth – which meant they judged themselves unworthy of the precious gift of the Gospel. They committed the one sin that can never be forgiven – they rejected Jesus!

At that moment, the Spirit led me to look at the leaders and declare, *"It was necessary that we first preach the word of God to you Jews. But since you have rejected it and judged yourselves unworthy of eternal life, we will offer it to the Gentiles. For the Lord gave us this command when He said, 'I have made you a light to the Gentiles, to bring salvation to the farthest corners of the earth.'"*[(8)]

• • •

The Gentiles present began to rejoice and thank the Lord for His goodness and mercy. As the unbelieving Jews watched, many of the Gentiles who had been appointed to eternal life confessed their belief that day. We went to a nearby stream and baptized them. When the rest of the people in the city heard what had happened, the Lord's message spread among them and throughout the entire region.

19

Then the Jews … incited a mob against Paul and Barnabas and ran them out of town. So they shook the dust from their feet as a sign of rejection and went to the town of Iconium.[1]

* * *

The Jewish leaders' jealousy continued to grow, as not only Gentiles were drawn to God's Word, but also more Jews were responding as well. The leaders decided they needed to stop us.

A city official named Quintus had become a follower of Jesus soon after we arrived in the city. He was a rising leader of this young and growing church. He confided in me that other city officials were being pressured by the Jewish leaders along with several influential women whose support they had garnered. They were demanding that Barnabas and I be forcefully ejected from the city. Quintus said the city officials were considering giving in to their ultimatum to appease them.

Quintus repeatedly told the officials about the changes for good he was seeing in the lives of those turning to Jesus. He explained that what was happening was good for the city. He reminded them Barnabas and I were not doing anything to incite violence; rather, it was the Jewish leaders who were guilty of that.

When the religious leaders saw the city officials were not taking action, they took measures into their own hands and incited a mob against us. The officials soon realized they had to choose between supporting the Jewish leaders and the mob or us. The former would be politically beneficial, the latter would not. Ignoring Quintus's pleas, they joined the mob to unceremoniously usher us out of the city.

As we stood on the outskirts of the city shaking the dust off our feet, we also took solace in knowing the Spirit of God would continue to guide this new church in His truth. We had already seen how Quintus and others were being raised up to help lead the church. With that assurance in mind, we set out for the city of Iconium.

On our first Sabbath in the city, Barnabas and I went to the synagogue. The Holy Spirit spoke through us with such power that numerous Jews and Gentiles believed that day. But like we had seen in Antioch of Pisidia, the religious leaders immediately began to stir up trouble, making false and evil accusations against us.

Over the next several days, the Spirit reminded us that greater is He who is in us than he who is in the world! As we continued to preach the Good News, the Lord proved that we were His witnesses by giving us the power to do miraculous signs and wonders. Many were healed, and many believed. Surprisingly though, that seemed to divide the people even more.

We woke up before dawn one morning to the news that a mob was headed our way to stone us. I immediately thought back to the days when I had led such a mob. As we debated whether to stay or go, the Spirit made it clear we should leave at once. We abruptly departed and traveled a short distance south to the city of Lystra.

It was early in the week when we arrived, so we decided to begin preaching in the city square near the synagogue. As we were preparing, we noticed a young man with crippled feet sitting beneath a sycamore tree. As I began to preach, I could see he was listening intently to every word. Soon I realized I was no longer looking at anyone but him. The Spirit impressed upon me that this young man had the faith to be healed.

Even though I was some distance away, I looked into his eyes and called out, "*Stand up!*"[2] Spectators in front of me turned their heads to follow my stare. For a moment, time stood still. Then suddenly, the young man jumped to his feet and began walking!

People in the crowd began to shout. "We know this young man. We know his father and his mother. His father brings him here each day. His name is Timothy. We have known him since he was a child! He has been crippled since birth!"

They turned to one another and said, "*These men are gods in human form!*"[3] As they pointed to Barnabas they said, "This one is Zeus, and the shorter man is Hermes! Send messengers to the temple of Zeus with a message to prepare sacrifices. The gods have seen fit to enter into our midst. We must prepare to worship them!"

Barnabas and I reacted by tearing our cloaks in dismay and crying out, "*Friends, why are you doing this? We are merely human beings – just like you! We have come to bring you the Good News that you should turn from these worthless things and turn to the living God, who made heaven and earth, the sea, and everything in them. In the past He permitted all the nations to go their own ways, but He never left them without evidence of Himself and His goodness. For instance, He sends you rain and good crops and gives you food and joyful hearts.*"[4]

• • •

The crowd seemed to ignore our pleas, but finally we convinced them not to offer sacrifices to us. And yet, they continued to shout and work themselves into a frenzy. The longer Barnabas and I stood there, the worse it got. As we started to leave, the young man who had been healed came to us and said, "Follow me!"

The crowd parted and allowed us to leave with the young man, despite their continuing debate over who we were. When we arrived at the young man's home, a woman about our age – whom I gathered was the young man's mother – met us at the door. She gave Barnabas and me a puzzled look and then turned to her son. "Timothy, you are walking!" she shouted. "How can this be?!?" Then she added, thoughtfully, "Unless God has answered our prayers!"

She embraced her son, and they praised God for His goodness. An older woman scurried into the room to see what was happening. When she saw the two, she began to weep and exclaimed, "Praise be to Jehovah God!"

After a while the two women turned their attention to Barnabas and me. "Timothy, who are these men?" the younger woman asked.

"I do not know their names, Mother," he answered. "But this one was preaching outside of the synagogue," he said, pointing to me. "He said the Messiah has come, and His name is Jesus. He told us Jesus came to make all things new. As he spoke, I began to believe the One of whom they were speaking could make me new. I believed He could make me walk. So when this man looked at me and said, '*Stand up!*'[(2)] I knew what I must do. I felt strength in my legs I have never felt, and I knew Jesus had healed me. And even though I don't know the names of these men, I have them to thank!"

• • •

All eyes were on Barnabas and me when I spoke up. "My name is Paul, and my companion's name is Barnabas. But we are due no thanks. You have been healed by the One who created you … the Giver of Life … the One who has made all things new again through the death and resurrection of His Son. Jehovah God has healed you today, and to Him alone do you owe your thanks!"

The women joined Timothy in giving praise to God. Timothy introduced the ladies as his mother, Eunice, and his grandmother, Lois. Both were Jews and devout in their faith. They had prayed for Timothy's healing since his birth, and today they had seen the answer to those prayers.

Timothy's father had heard what happened to his son and came home to see for himself. His name was Neoptolemus, and he was a Gentile. And though he did not share the faith of his wife and mother-in-law, he rejoiced that his son could now walk and was grateful for however it happened.

One of their neighbors came to tell us a mob was gathering outside so we stepped out to see what they wanted. Some Jews had arrived in the city from Antioch of Pisidia and Iconium, and were spreading venomous lies about me. Neoptolemus attempted to calm their anger. "My friends and neighbors," he said, "I do not know what is true and what is not true about these men. But I do know my son, whom many of you have known since he was born, has been healed! He who was crippled can now walk. And these men had something to do with that. Leave them alone. They are guests in my home!"

But the crowd would not listen to reason. They pushed Neoptolemus out of the way and dragged me out of the city. Evidently, the Jews who had incited them had not mentioned Barnabas, so he was left unharmed. When we arrived at the edge of the city, the men picked up stones and began to hurl them at me. My thoughts turned to Stephen and the day I had been a party to stoning him outside the gates of Jerusalem. I turned my gaze toward heaven as I had seen him do … and I looked up into the face of

Jesus. Everything around me grew dim, and in a few moments, I lay on the ground as one who was dead.

Eventually, the mob disbanded and returned to town. They left my body in a heap amid the thrown stones. Barnabas, Timothy, and his family soon arrived but thought I had died. I cannot say for sure whether I was dead. All I know is I heard the voice of Jesus say, "Paul, the work I have for you is not finished. Stand up!"

Everyone was amazed as I slowly rose to my feet. I looked at Timothy and said, "My son, when Jesus tells us to stand up, we can do no less!" Together, we all walked back to Timothy's home. A few people stared at us as we passed by, but no one said anything – and the mob never returned. Barnabas and I stayed with the family that night and departed for Derbe the next morning, but not until we baptized Timothy, Eunice, Lois – and Neoptolemus.

We spent several weeks in Derbe preaching the Good News and many came to faith. Barnabas and I encouraged them to continue in the truth and to share it with others. By the time we departed, there was a thriving church in Derbe.

We returned to Lystra and remained there for several weeks preaching the Gospel. No further mobs formed, and no one made any attempt to come against us – but many came to believe in Jesus. We stayed with Neoptolemus and his family and marveled at how they had grown in their faith during our absence. We strengthened the believers and encouraged them all in their faith.

"You will pass through many tribulations in your journey with Jesus into the kingdom of God," I said. "*Everyone who wants to live a godly life in Christ Jesus will suffer persecution. But you must remain faithful to the things you have been taught. You know they are true, and you know you can trust those who taught you.*"[(5)]

• • •

It seemed right to appoint Neoptolemus and Timothy, together with two other men, to be elders of the church in Lystra. Before we left, we prayed for them while fasting and turned them over to the care of the Lord. We reminded them to keep their eyes on Jesus, the Author and Finisher of their faith.

From there we returned to Iconium. We were encouraged that those who had believed during our previous stay in the city had continued to grow in their faith and understanding. In a place where some had threatened to stone Barnabas and me, the Spirit was growing a healthy, vibrant church. It reminded us we must be faithful to do what God has called us to do – but the results depend on the works of the Spirit, not on our works.

After several weeks, we made our way back to Antioch in Pisidia. Quintus was excited to report that despite the best efforts of the Jewish leaders and others, the church was continuing to grow. Most of the residents had grown weary of the leaders' hostility and were embracing the many positive changes they were witnessing in the lives of those following Jesus.

Again, we saw how the seeds of the Gospel were thriving even in persecution. We remained with them for several weeks to strengthen them in their understanding and challenge them in their continuing faithfulness.

"You know, dear brothers and sisters, how badly Barnabas and I were treated by some in your city," I proclaimed. "*Yet our God gave us the courage to declare His Good News to you boldly, even though we were surrounded by many who opposed us. For we speak as messengers who have been approved by God to be entrusted with the Good News.*[(6)] You also have been entrusted with that Good News. *Be faithful to preach the Word of God. Be persistent, whether the time is favorable or not.*"[(7)]

• • •

The Lord came to me in a dream one night and told me it was time to return to the church in Antioch of Syria. This journey had come to an end. The next morning, as I began to tell Barnabas, he interrupted me and told me the Lord had come to him in a dream as well – with the same message.

A few days later, we concluded our work and departed for the coast. We passed through Perga and traveled on to Attalia, staying in each place only a few days to preach. In Attalia, we boarded a ship and set sail to Antioch. It was a four-day journey by sea. The waters were calm, and the voyage was uneventful. We had no idea what was awaiting us in Antioch, but the Lord permitted those days to refresh and strengthen us in preparation.

And by the grace of God, when the ship docked, we had the joy of baptizing the entire ship's crew as a testimony to their newfound faith in Jesus!

* * *

20

Finally, they returned by ship to Antioch of Syria, where their journey had begun. The believers there had entrusted them to the grace of God to do the work they had now completed.(1)

* * *

Almost two years had passed since the church in Antioch had commissioned Barnabas and me to go. They had been an integral part of our mission – providing our financial support and undergirding our work through prayer. They had prayed for open doors through which the Gospel could be spread, for anointing in our preaching, for the nurture of new believers, for the new churches that were birthed, for safety and health in our travels, and for every aspect of our journey. Now that we had returned, our first responsibility was to report to them all God had accomplished through their prayers.

Though we looked the worse for wear after our journey, we had barely entered the city when a couple of the brothers recognized us. They ran to embrace us. They called out to other brothers and sisters who were nearby – even new believers we did not recognize. They all rejoiced in our return, and we were strengthened by their enthusiastic welcome.

. . .

Soon we arrived at Manaen's home. He immediately sent word of our return to Lucius, Simeon, and Luke, who quickly joined us. I knew they wanted to hear our report, but first we wanted to hear what had transpired in Antioch. We had seen the new construction throughout the city. There was little evidence remaining of the earthquake's wrath.

Manaen told us the church had thrived during the city's rebuilding. In fact, the church had grown so large it was now gathering in multiple locations. Manaen and the others were convinced God was rewarding the two-fold faithfulness of the church. First, they had been obedient in reaching out to people with overwhelming needs following the earthquake. Because of this, God had graciously opened additional doors.

"We also believe God rewarded our faithfulness in sending out you two men to share the Good News in places where it had not yet been heard," Manaen continued. He said the church was obedient to Jesus's command to make disciples not only where we live, but also in the places where we do not live – to the ends of the earth. "We pray He will find us faithful in everything He sets before us to do!"

It was Lucius who changed the direction of our conversation when he asked, "Where is the young man who traveled with you?"

We knew the church had been praying for him as well. Barnabas was the first to reply. "About two months into our journey, John Mark became increasingly concerned about the welfare of his widowed mother in Jerusalem. He believed he needed to return to care for her. When we arrived in Perga, he departed for Jerusalem. Though Paul and I were sorry to see him go, we knew we must continue on our way to Antioch in Pisidia."

. . .

Honestly, I would have replied to Lucius's question much differently from Barnabas. He and I had discussed John Mark numerous times since he left. I believed John Mark had abandoned us and had been ruled by fear instead of the Spirit. I refused to condone his action, but Barnabas was much more forgiving.

My convictions were that we should complete the work God has entrusted to us by His grace. John Mark failed to do that. I also thought this was a teachable moment for the church of Antioch. But I decided this was not the time or place to continue my debate with Barnabas, so I remained silent.

Later that night, a large gathering of the church assembled for Barnabas and me to report on our journey. "You entrusted us," I began, "to the grace of God. By His grace, God set us apart for the journey. By His grace, He went before us to prepare hearts to receive the seeds of His Gospel. By His grace, He provided us with "people of peace" at each synagogue along the way who invited us to speak and thereby opened the door for us to preach the Good News.

"By His grace, He gave us power to defeat a sorcerer who was being used as an instrument of Satan. By His grace, He granted us favor with the governor of Cyprus as we witnessed his salvation and experienced his favor as we continued to travel throughout the island. By His grace, He opened a wider door for the spreading of the Gospel among the Gentiles in Antioch of Pisidia and beyond. By His grace, He brought glory to His name through the healing of a young, crippled man in Lystra. By His grace, He raised me up from the ground after I was stoned and left for dead. By His grace, God raised up elders in every church planted. And by His grace, He permitted us to safely return to Antioch. In these ways, and in so many others, the Spirit of God has gone before us in our travels and led us through every twist and turn. You prayed for grace, and God extended His inexhaustible supply!"

It was important for the church members to hear our account. They needed to know how their prayers had been answered. They needed to know how God had worked through them for the advancement of His mission. They needed the opportunity to praise and glorify God through their worship and thanksgiving over the great things He had done.

The church also needed to love on us. We had returned to them weary and somewhat beaten and bruised. We were physically, emotionally, and spiritually depleted. We needed them to fill us back up, to encourage us, to minister to our woundedness and weariness. The church needed to be an oasis at the end of what had been a long and vigorous journey.

But we also knew the ministering went both ways. We needed to pour ourselves into the church, using our experiences to better equip them to reach the nations right there in Antioch. We needed to help the church prepare and support those whom God would call in the future to send out from within the body. We needed to help the church see its ever-growing role in carrying out Christ's Great Commission to the nations.

We hadn't been back in Antioch long when the apostle Peter came for a visit. The church was inspired by his teaching, and I was encouraged to hear how the Spirit of the Lord had directed him to bring the message of the Gospel to the Gentiles. I was pleased to see he did not allow himself to be restricted by the Jewish food laws when he was eating with his Gentile brothers.

However, about two weeks later, several other men from the church in Jerusalem arrived. I noticed Peter's actions changed immediately. He no longer dined with his Gentile brothers but separated from them like the other Jewish brothers. Soon, the other Jews began doing the same thing – including Barnabas.

I had no choice but to confront Peter in front of the others, saying, "*Since you, a Jew by birth, have discarded the Jewish laws and are living like a Gentile, why are you now trying to make these Gentiles follow the Jewish traditions?*"[2]

• • •

Gratefully, Peter, Barnabas, and the others saw the error of their ways and asked for forgiveness from the Lord, from me, and from their Gentile brothers. It reminded me how easily we can get caught up in our religious traditions and lose sight of the truths of the Gospel.

A few months later, I received an unexpected visit from Andreas of Salamis. Antioch was one of the stops along the route of his current trading voyage. He had set sail five days earlier from Perga. He had arrived in Antioch to trade for a large quantity of oil of lilies. The oil is a precious commodity produced in and around Antioch. It is known not only for its use in the making of perfumes, but also – as Luke would later tell me – as a soothing balm used by physicians for the treatment of a variety of emotional maladies, such as anxiety and depression.

After he caught me up on all the news of his family, his crew, and the church in Salamis, he explained the main reason for his visit. He had not known I was in Antioch until just a few days earlier. While in Perga, he was approached by a young man who had a letter he needed delivered to a Paul of Tarsus who was now in Antioch. The young man had been told Andreas was soon departing for Antioch.

"When I told the young man I knew Paul of Tarsus," Andreas explained, "he was beside himself with joy. We soon discovered you had led both of us to place our faith and trust in Jesus – and that we were brothers in Christ. I welcomed the opportunity to seek you out when I got to Antioch. So here I am!"

"What was the young man's name?" I asked.

"Timothy," Andreas replied.

I thanked God for this double portion of His grace and goodness – a visit with Andreas and a letter from Timothy. Inside the world of God's divine grace, it most certainly is a "small world." After Andreas went on his way, I stopped to read the letter. My joy quickly turned to sorrow as he described what was taking place among the believers in Galatia. I immediately set out to find Manaen. I needed to send a letter of reply, and my physical infirmities would prevent me from doing so. I would need him to record my words.

And so I began:

"From: Paul, an apostle
To: The churches of Galatia
May God the Father and our Lord Jesus Christ give you grace and peace. Jesus gave His life for our sins, just as God our Father planned, in order to rescue us from this evil world in which we live. All glory to God forever and ever! Amen."[3]

The churches in Galatia had turned away from their journey of faith in Christ and had now embarked on a course of "good works." They were turning from the grace of Christ and redirecting their attention to the stipulations of the law. The church was attempting to receive God's approval by keeping the law versus walking with Him by faith. I reminded them in my letter they must die to the law and be crucified with Christ.

"I have been crucified with Christ," I said. *"It is no longer I who live, but Christ who lives in me. And the life I now live in the flesh I live by faith in the Son of God, who loved me and gave Himself for me.*[4] Righteousness is only obtained by the grace of God through the death, burial, and resurrection of Jesus, and not through any works that we may do, or attempt to do."

I went on to tell them, *"Christ has truly set us free. Now make sure that you stay free, and don't get tied up again in slavery to the law.*[5] *I advise you to live according to your new life in the Holy Spirit.*[6] Do not walk under the bondage of the law, neither should you follow the desires of your sinful nature. Allow the Holy Spirit to control your lives, because when He does, *He will produce this kind of fruit in us: love, joy, peace, patience, kindness, goodness, faithfulness, gentleness and self-control."*[7]

. . .

As I came to the close of my letter, I took the pen from Manaen and personally wrote:

"Notice what large letters I use as I write these closing words in my own handwriting.
Those who are trying to force you to [follow the law] want to look good to others. They don't want to be persecuted for teaching that the cross of Christ alone can save. And even those who advocate [strict obedience to the law] don't keep the whole law themselves. They only want you to [do so] so they can boast about it and claim you as their disciples. As for me, may I never boast about anything except the cross of our Lord Jesus Christ. Because of that cross, my interest in this world has been crucified, and the world's interest in me has also died. It doesn't matter whether we have [obeyed the law] or not. What counts is whether we have been transformed into a new creation. May God's peace and mercy be upon all who live by this principle; they are the new people of God.
From now on, don't let anyone trouble me with these things. For I bear on my body the scars that show I belong to Jesus.
Dear brothers and sisters, may the grace of our Lord Jesus Christ be with your spirit. Amen."[8]

It was early the next morning when we finished the letter. But the cock had not yet crowed, so I hurriedly set out to find Andreas's ship. I knew he planned to set sail that day, and I wanted to be certain he had my letter in hand. When I arrived at the docks, he and his crew were already busily preparing to set sail. I charged him with the responsibility of seeking out Timothy upon his return voyage and delivering my letter to him personally. I then bade my faithful brother farewell.

. . .

A few days later, some men arrived from Judea. They immediately began to teach the Gentile believers, *"Unless you are circumcised as required by the law of Moses, you cannot be saved."*(9)

Barnabas and I immediately began to refute them. These were the same seeds of division being sewn among the Galatian churches. I knew from my time with Jesus on Mount Sinai He was not placing that bondage on the Gentile believers. His cross had paved the way for them to enter into relationship with Him – and nothing could or should be added to that expression of His grace.

Our debate became lengthy and forceful. By the end of the day, the other elders and I knew we needed to send a delegation to the apostles and elders of the church in Jerusalem to bring this matter to a final resolution. Our elders and the church prayed, setting apart Barnabas and me, together with some of the other believers, to go to Jerusalem.

Along the way we stopped in Sidon and Tyre, as well as Samaria, reporting on the work of the Spirit of God among the Gentiles in Syria. At each stop, our brothers and sisters rejoiced with us over the good news. Though I knew salvation was the Lord's work, I feared that a wrong decision by the apostles and elders in Jerusalem could stifle further movement of His Spirit among the Gentiles.

The night before we were to arrive in Jerusalem, the Lord reminded me the debate would not be won by my – or anyone else's – eloquence of words. This was His church! These were His followers! And His work would be accomplished in His way according to His will! I simply needed to trust Him … and watch Him do His work!

To that end, we traveled on to Jerusalem the next day.

* * *

21

Some of the men who had been Pharisees before their conversion stood up and declared that all Gentile converts must be circumcised and be required to follow the law of Moses.[1]

* * *

We went directly to Mnason's home when we arrived in Jerusalem. I was pleased to learn he had recently been made one of the elders of the church. We explained the purpose of our visit and our desire to meet with the leadership of the church. Mnason sent messages to James and the others to let them know of our intent, and they quickly sent their reply for us to come meet with them. We were warmly welcomed by the entire church, including Peter, James, and the other apostles and elders.

They invited us to share about what God was doing in and through the church in Antioch as well as on our recent travels in Asia. Barnabas and I were as blessed as they were as we recounted all the things God had accomplished. Everyone joined with us as we gave praise to the Lord.

. . .

It was getting late, so Peter suggested we stop for the night so everyone could rest, and we would resume the next day. But I could not sleep. Since it was a beautiful spring night, I decided to walk across the valley to the gardens I knew Jesus had frequented. Barnabas and Mnason offered to join me, but I told them I needed time alone for a walk with the Master.

As I passed through the vineyards, a light breeze stirred the leaves. It sounded similar to a whisper. But the longer I listened, I realized it *was* a whisper. My Lord was speaking to me – a quiet voice that didn't need volume to command authority … or my attention.

It had been years since He and I had walked together in the cool of the evenings like this in the Arabian wilderness. Much had passed since then. But His clear voice and calming presence were unmistakable. I know His Spirit is always with me wherever I go – whether it's on a storm-tossed sea, amid a pile of rocks in Lystra where I was left for dead, or in a prison in Seleucia. I know He never leaves me nor forsakes me. But there was something about this moment in the garden. It was His reminder to me that He is God. This is His church. And I am to watch Him … as He leads *His* church.

The time passed quickly – too quickly. When the sun began to rise, I headed back to resume our meeting with the church leaders. Barnabas and I, together with the other brothers from the church in Antioch, continued with our reports into the afternoon. There was no mistaking how the Spirit of God was at work drawing the Gentiles to Himself.

When we were done, some of the believers who had been Pharisees before coming to faith in Jesus, stood up to plead their case. One of the men, by the name of Joazar, acted as chief spokesman.

"Our brothers, Saul and Barnabas, have stirred our hearts with the good news of how men and women throughout Syria, Cyprus, and Asia are turning from their wicked ways and becoming followers of the Messiah," he said. "It is just as the Master promised before He ascended into heaven to sit on the right hand of His Father. We are to make disciples of people, not only in Jerusalem and Judea, but also in Samaria and to the ends of the earth. He is fulfilling His promise to our patriarch Abraham when He said, *'This is My covenant with you. I will make you the father of not just one nation, but a multitude of nations!'*(2)

"These men and women we have heard about from Saul, Barnabas, and the others have become Jewish Christians just like the rest of us. They have now become a part of God's chosen people through His Son, Jesus. Our Messiah is the Son of God, but He is also of the seed of Abraham. Those who choose to follow Him must do so as all the rest of us have. They must enter into the Abrahamic covenant just as God has said: *'Your part of this agreement is to obey the terms of this covenant. You and all your descendants have this continual responsibility. Each male among you must be circumcised.'*(3) We do not say this – Jehovah God has said it! The Gentiles cannot become Christians without first becoming Jews. They cannot become followers of Jesus without first entering into the covenant the Father made with Abraham."

Some of the other men spoke up in agreement. The debate continued long into the evening. Finally, James said, "This matter must now be discussed and decided by the apostles and the elders. Join us in praying that God grants us wisdom and understanding to walk in this matter according to His perfect and holy will."

The next day the apostles and elders met as a council to discuss the issue. Barnabas and I were permitted to attend, but we were instructed to do so silently as the others debated the question.

The council was seeking to resolve both an essential doctrinal issue as well as an issue of fellowship. Gentile culture is characterized by idolatry and immorality. These leaders knew they needed to admonish the Gentile believers to *live as citizens of heaven, conducting themselves in a manner worthy of the Good News of Christ.*(4) That meant the Gentile believers must learn to walk in the righteousness of Christ and abstain from any practice of idolatry or immorality – or even the appearance of it. Thus, they needed to not eat food that has been presented to idols.

To the Jewish believers, the council was seeking to make clear that God has not placed the burden of the law on Gentiles – and they, as Jews, have no need to do so either. Jesus's blood was shed for Jew and Gentile alike. One did not need to become like the other to partake in the grace of God. Rather, each needed to receive the gift of God by faith.

Also, Jewish and Gentile believers needed to act in a way that promoted the unity of the Gospel. The church now was a mixture of Jewish-background believers and Gentile-background believers. And since fellowship and the sharing of meals had become a significant part of the church gathering together, the council knew the Gentile believers needed to make dietary concessions in deference to their Jewish brothers and sisters. They needed to abstain from eating blood or meat from animals that died by strangulation. Those concessions would promote unity within the body and present a united witness to a lost world.

Mnason spoke up as a voice of reason and wisdom saying, "Jesus told His followers the world would know we are His disciples by the love we have for one another. God has opened a wide and effective door of ministry for the church to take the Gospel of His grace to a condemned world. But there are forces at work that want to close that door. The enemy would have us emphasize those things that divide us and divert us. We must learn to listen to the Word of God and the Spirit of God and hold those alone as our authority, that we might walk through that wide and effective door ... together."

The sun set and rose several times before the discussion was brought to a conclusion. Peter declared the discussion to be over when he stood and said, *"Brothers, you all know that God chose me from among you some time ago to preach to the Gentiles so that they could hear the Good News and believe. God knows people's hearts, and He confirmed that He accepts Gentiles by giving them the Holy Spirit, just as He did to us. He made no distinction between us and them, for He cleansed their hearts through faith. So why are you now challenging God by burdening the Gentile believers with a yoke that neither we nor our ancestors were able to bear? We believe that we are all saved the same way, by the undeserved grace of the Lord Jesus."*(5)

After Peter sat down, James turned to Barnabas and me and asked us to tell the group again about the miraculous signs and wonders God had done through us among the Gentiles. By the time we finished, there was no question that God makes no distinction between Jew and Gentile. His Spirit is at work in both to cleanse hearts and draw each through faith to Himself.

James was the last to stand, saying, *"Brothers, listen to me. Peter has told you about the time God first visited the Gentiles to take from them a people for Himself. And this conversion of Gentiles is exactly what the prophets predicted. As it is written: 'Afterward I will return and restore the fallen house of David. I will rebuild its ruins and restore it, so that the rest of humanity might seek the Lord, including the Gentiles – all those I have called to be Mine. The Lord has spoken – He who made these things known so long ago.'*

"And so my judgment is that we should not make it difficult for the Gentiles who are turning to God. Instead, we should write and tell them to abstain from eating food offered to idols, from sexual immorality, from eating the meat of strangled animals, and from consuming blood. For these laws of Moses have been preached in Jewish synagogues in every city on every Sabbath for many generations."(6)

I found myself thinking back to the assurance Jesus had given me in the garden a few nights earlier. Jesus had again just led His church. We are His body under His headship made up of many members from different backgrounds – but all according to His purpose. We will not always agree. Our differences will never be resolved by argument. They will be settled as we follow Jesus and submit ourselves under His Lordship! Sadly, I thought of my childhood friend Ashmus. Oh, how he loved passionate debate and thought it was the solution to every problem. But in the end, he failed to follow the only One who truly has the answer. Gratefully, the men in this room had not made that same mistake.

The apostles and elders prepared a letter for the church in Antioch and chose two delegates to return with us to report on the decision that had been made. One of the men chosen was Judas Barsabbas. Since the betrayal of Jesus, it had become common for men in Jerusalem named Judas to include their second name. The name Judas, which had once signified uprightness in honor of men like Judas Maccabeus, had since become stained by the acts of the betrayer Judas Iscariot. Those who bore that name and knew of Iscariot's treachery – whether they be believer or nonbeliever – wanted to take measures to disassociate themselves from the shadow that name now cast.

But I learned on our journey back to Antioch that a part of Barsabbas's story had further connection to Iscariot beyond his surname. After Jesus ascended to sit at the right hand of the Father, 120 of His followers had gone to an upper room to await the arrival of the Holy Spirit as Jesus had promised. Barsabbas and his brother had been part of that group. As they waited, Peter had announced that a man must be chosen to take Iscariot's place among the apostles.

During His time with the disciples, Jesus had once told them, *"I assure you that when the world is made new and the Son of Man sits upon His glorious throne, you who have been My followers will also sit on twelve thrones, judging the twelve tribes of Israel."*[(7)] Not knowing how soon Jesus would return, the apostles believed that the twelfth position needed to be filled immediately in order for them to be ready. So, they had nominated two men from whom they would ultimately choose one.

These men had also been with Jesus throughout His ministry, witnessing His miracles, His death, and His resurrection. They had numbered themselves among the seventy men Jesus had sent out in pairs to preach in the villages. One of those was Matthias – the one who was subsequently chosen by lot to become the twelfth. The man not chosen was Judas

Barsabbas's older brother, Joseph. Both brothers – sons of Sabbas – had numbered themselves among the seventy and now served as elders of the church in Jerusalem.

The second man chosen to travel to Antioch with us was Silas. He was a servant-leader and teacher in the church. I knew little about him, other than the fact he reminded me of a spiritual giant of a man I had once met. And the more I observed him during our trip, the more convinced I became that he also was a spiritual giant of a man.

After we arrived in Antioch and assembled the church, Silas opened the letter and read:

"This letter is from the apostles and elders, your brothers in Jerusalem. It is written to the Gentile believers in Antioch, Syria, and Cilicia. Greetings!

"We understand that some men from Jerusalem have troubled you and upset you with their teaching, but we did not send them! So we decided, having come to complete agreement, to send you official representatives, along with our beloved Barnabas and Paul, who have risked their lives for the name of our Lord Jesus Christ. We are sending Judas and Silas to confirm what we have decided concerning your question.

"For it seemed good to the Holy Spirit and to us to lay no greater burden on you than these few requirements: You must abstain from eating food offered to idols, from consuming blood or the meat of strangled animals, and from sexual immorality. If you do this, you will do well. Farewell."[8]

The church joyfully received the letter, and any hint of division evaporated. They rejoiced in the affirmation that we are one body, with one Lord, one faith, and one baptism. Judas and Silas remained with us in Antioch for several days before returning to Jerusalem. The church sent them off with words of encouragement and blessing for their brothers and sisters in Jerusalem.

• • •

Barnabas and I continued the work God had given us – teaching and nurturing the believers in Antioch. After several months, the Spirit of God stirred my heart to return to the cities where we had previously preached the Good News. They needed further encouragement, just as Antioch did.

While we were making plans, Barnabas said, "I have sent word to John Mark for him to come join us again in our travels. I want to complete the promise I made to his mother to disciple him. When we were in Jerusalem a few months ago, I took the opportunity to visit with him and his mother. John Mark is very contrite for the abrupt way he abandoned us in Perga. I sensed his regret over what he had done and his desire to make it right. I believe he has learned from his mistake and will be of even greater assistance to us in this journey. He now has a much better understanding of what to expect, and that will work to his credit. He should arrive in a matter of days – just in time for us to depart."

I'm not sure what Barnabas expected me to say. Did he think I would simply forget what John Mark had done? Did Barnabas not realize that this journey was much more important than any one young man? We could not be distracted from the mission by one who so easily could faint and walk away! I admired Barnabas's commitment to Mary and his desire to mentor the boy. But we could not take that chance with this trip. The sake of the mission was too great! Our mandate to preach the Good News among the Gentiles of Asia and Europe could not be put at risk. No! John Mark would not be traveling with us!

"What do you expect me to tell him when he arrives in a few days?" Barnabas asked.

"Tell him he can't go!" I replied. "Tell him we can only bring people with us who are committed to finish the race. Tell him we cannot be certain he will endure, and the mission is too great to take such a risk! Tell him to go back home, to actively serve with the leaders in the church in Jerusalem and grow under their teaching. Tell him he will be surrounded by men who walked with Jesus, and they are more than adequately equipped to disciple him!"

Barnabas was incredulous. We had disagreed from time to time – but never this adamantly. He knew I was not going to soften or change my mind. And yet, the lad would arrive in a few days. What was Barnabas to do? He refused to send him back home. So, we came to the only conclusion we could. We decided to part ways.

When John Mark arrived in Antioch, he and Barnabas set sail for Cyprus. There was much work still to be done there. By their doing so, I would be able to concentrate my time through Cilicia and Asia. But I knew I needed a companion for my journey – someone with maturity and determination. It was then I realized the Spirit of God had already provided me with the answer. I knew the man He had chosen to join me on this mission.

I immediately sent word to Jerusalem. My written message simply said, "Silas, come join me! You and I leave for Asia in a few days. I don't know when we will return. Come quickly! Paul."

* * *

22

So Paul and Silas traveled throughout Syria and Cilicia to strengthen the churches there.[1]

* * *

The elders of the church in Antioch laid hands on Silas and me, committing us and our journey to the Lord, and sent us on our way. I was grateful for the prayer covering of these brothers and this church. Though I knew the Spirit of the Lord was leading and going with us every step of the way, it was comforting to know we were faithfully being undergirded by the believers in Antioch.

For the first few days of our journey, I kept thinking back to my conversation with Barnabas. I regretted the rift between us. He had been a good friend and encourager when few others were. I would miss him.

But I also knew it was not the Lord's intention for John Mark to be part of this journey – not only because of his earlier abandonment, but I also believed he lacked the maturity needed for the path God would be leading me to take. I had peace about my decision and rested in the sovereignty of God that it was His plan for Barnabas and me to part ways.

At the same time, I was grateful for the opportunity to get better acquainted with Silas. Though the Spirit let me know he was to be my companion on this trip, I had no idea of the ways God had already equipped and prepared him for our journey.

Silas told me he was born in Alexandria. His parents were Hellenistic Jews who gave him the Hebrew name "Silas" and the Roman name "Silvanus." His family, just like mine, had been successful merchants for multiple generations. Thus, his parents had earned their Roman citizenship, and as a result, he had received his at birth. He had been an exceptional student, excelling in all his coursework, including the Hebrew Scriptures. As a young man, he traveled to Jerusalem with his father's blessing to sit under the teaching of some of the most learned Hellenistic rabbis.

"While in synagogue," he continued, "I met another passionate young man named Stephanos. The two of us fervently discussed and debated the Scriptures – with one another and with the rabbis. I will confess that Stephanos was even better versed in the Scriptures than I, so he routinely prevailed in our debates. However, we were both earnestly seeking a deeper understanding, and that quickly drew us together as friends. Those were tumultuous days in Jerusalem. Jesus was at the peak of His popularity with the people and greatly feared by the religious leaders.

"Their fear had led them to make their diabolical plans resulting in the crucifixion of Jesus. It wasn't until He was led to the hill called Golgotha that Stephanos and I really began to pay attention to Him and to His teachings. We watched as events unfolded throughout that day. We were puzzled like everyone else when the sun grew dark for three hours at midday. We felt an unexplainable heaviness when we learned He was dead.

. . .

"The world seemed somehow different during the days immediately following His death until the beginning of the next week. We heard rumors Jesus had risen from the dead. I, at first, dismissed them as preposterous lies; but Stephanos was less certain the rumors were false.

"One morning, Stephanos had an encounter with a man named Clopas. He introduced himself as a follower of Jesus. Stephanos had no idea the man was also a part of Jesus's family. He told Stephanos about the encounter he'd had with the risen Savior along the road to Emmaus on the third day after He was crucified. His account was so convincing that Stephanos believed and became a follower of Jesus.

"When he told me later what he had done, I could not believe my ears. How could my learned friend fall prey to such a fabricated hoax? But the more we discussed the prophecies, the facts we knew about Jesus, and the account Stephanos had heard, I began to question if it were true, too.

"We eventually met the apostles Peter and John. Soon we met James, who as the half brother of Jesus, had surprisingly only recently come to believe in Him since His resurrection. It was then I surrendered my life to Jesus by faith. A few weeks later, we gathered with others on the mount outside of Bethany to watch Jesus ascend into the heavens.

"Stephanos had always had the capacity to understand truths before I did and then to help me discover them. In many ways, Stephanos discipled me – not only in His words but also in His actions.

"When the Holy Spirit came on the Day of Pentecost, He filled us all with His presence – but I think Stephanos received a double portion. From that point forward, I saw him as a man filled to overflowing with faith and the Holy Spirit. He would often remind me that I too was indwelt by the Holy Spirit and also was full of faith. But in comparison to my friend, I always felt somewhat less so. Together, however, we would try to start conversations with some of the young men from our former synagogue so we could share Jesus with them. Side by side, we served the growing number of believers there in Jerusalem.

"Eventually, Peter and the other apostles were led by God to set aside Stephanos and six other men to distribute food to the Hellenistic widows in the growing church. I assisted him and he continued to help me learn and understand."

At that moment, it registered who the "spiritual giant of a man" Silas reminded me of – it was his friend, Stephanos, also known as Stephen. The man I had known … and helped to stone.

All this time, Silas knew I had been complicit in the martyrdom of his best friend. And yet, he never said a word. When he realized I was aware he knew, he said, "That man who helped stone my friend no longer lives. He is now in Christ. *He is a new creation. The old has passed away; behold the new has come. All this is from God, who through Christ reconciled us to Himself and gave us the ministry of reconciliation.*(2) He doesn't count our trespasses against us – and neither do I."

We stopped to embrace there on the road. I turned to my brother and received his forgiveness, his mercy, and his grace. I knew without a doubt the Spirit had orchestrated for the two of us to travel together so I might come to really know this man – who himself was full of faith and the Holy Spirit.

Two weeks later, having stopped in villages along the way to preach the Good News, we arrived in Tarsus. It had been four years since Barnabas had come there to take me to Antioch. In some respects it felt like a lifetime had passed, and in some ways, it truly had been! When we arrived at my home, Dinah and Reuben introduced me to their youngest child, Benjamin, who was now three years old. My oldest nephew, eighteen-year-old Hezron, was a good-looking young man, anxious to set out on his own life adventures. In the meantime, he had become a proficient tentmaker and was his father's assistant. Esther, age twelve, and Rachel, age seven, were becoming beautiful young ladies, just like their mother, and were a delight to behold.

We stayed with my family for two weeks, taking the time to teach and encourage the church. Arsakes, Reuben, and the other elders were delighted about the pronouncement from Jerusalem regarding Gentile believers. The church in Tarsus had become increasingly divided over those issues. In fact, later that evening when the church gathered to hear Silas read the letter, there was great rejoicing.

Time with them passed quickly, but we realized we needed to cross over into the province of Galatia to encourage the churches in Derbe and Lystra. At every stop, we shared the letter from the church in Jerusalem. It was always received with celebration.

In Lystra, I was grateful to reunite with Timothy, Neoptolemus, Eunice, and Lydia. They had become like extended members of my family, so our time together was as uplifting as my time had been with Dinah and her family.

Seeing Timothy's spiritual growth and maturity, and hearing the good report from the churches in Lystra and Derbe, I invited him to join Silas and me as we headed to Iconium. He would serve as our assistant, similar to what John Mark had done for Barnabas and me. Perhaps this was another reason God had led Barnabas and me to go separate ways – so I could further disciple Timothy as we traveled.

When Timothy made the decision to travel with us, with the blessing of his family and his church, he was immediately confronted with a crisis of belief. Since coming to faith, I too had personally experienced my own crises of belief on multiple occasions. I had found that God often permits us to face an unexpected obstacle or confront a difficult decision that reveals whether we truly trust God to lead us in what He has told us to do.

I believed in order for Timothy to join us he needed to be circumcised. Even though his mother was Jewish, his father was a Gentile. Neoptolemus had never seen any reason to circumcise his son.

It was a fair question when Neoptolemus asked me why his son needed to be circumcised. We had just read the letter to the church that no such requirement would be made of Gentile believers. As the son of a Gentile, his father wanted to know why I was making an exception for Timothy.

I tried to explain. God had called me to minister to both Jew and Gentile. If Timothy traveled with us, he would be helping to shepherd new believers to walk in unity with one another. I would be nurturing him in how to teach and shepherd the people, and he would be working with both Jews and Gentiles in the churches. If Timothy was not circumcised, it would create contention among the Jewish believers – and that contention would disrupt the unity of the body.

When I sat down with Timothy and his parents, I told them: "*Even though I am a free man with no master, I have become a slave to all people to bring many to Christ. When I was with the Jews, I lived like a Jew to bring the Jews to Christ. When I was with those who follow the Jewish law, I too lived under that law. Even though I am not subject to the law, I did this so I could bring to Christ those who are under the law. When I am with the Gentiles who do not follow the Jewish law, I too live apart from that law so I can bring them to Christ. But I do not ignore the law of God; I obey the law of Christ. When I am with those who are weak, I share their weakness, for I want to bring the weak to Christ. Yes, I try to find common ground with everyone, doing everything I can to save some. I do everything to spread the Good News and share in its blessings.*[3]

"Timothy and I could debate the issue with the Jewish believers that he is not under the law of Moses," I continued. "We could point to the decision by the elders in Jerusalem. But those energies would take away from our primary mission and expend our time to the detriment of our proclamation of the Gospel and the nurturing of the church."

. . .

At that point, Timothy spoke up. "If I am to be a servant of Christ to all the believers, it isn't the law of Moses I need to place myself under; but rather, the law of Christ. I know in this case I cannot follow Christ – by following Paul – if I am not circumcised. I cannot allow myself to be a stumbling block and faithfully serve my Lord."

As I listened to Timothy, I was filled with godly pride in this young man. He was learning to stand firm in his own faith with a heart to lead others well. I knew the Spirit of the Lord would use him mightily in the days ahead in an important role to spread the Gospel and expand and strengthen the churches.

I knew I could invest my life into his. It prompted me to tell him, "*What you have heard from me in the presence of many witnesses entrust to faithful men, who will be able to teach others also.*"(4)

We remained in Lystra for a few days so Timothy could heal from his circumcision before setting out on our journey farther west into Asia. Then, as we approached the western border, Silas and I were restrained by the Spirit of the Lord from entering the cities. Rather, He directed us to turn northward and go toward the provinces of Bithynia and Pontus. Though I had not visited those regions, Timothy told me some believers from Iconium had been there to share the Good News. This path would allow us to go into those cities to preach and to encourage the believers.

But, as we approached that border, the Spirit again redirected us and turned us back toward the west. We soon found ourselves in the seaport town of Troas on the shore of the Aegean Sea. When we set out from Antioch, I never envisioned we would go to these regions. But God obviously had other plans.

I also never imagined these changes when I invited Timothy to travel with us. I had told his parents we would be traveling to the churches in Galatia, Phrygia, Pamphylia, and Asia, which were all within a 160-kilometer radius of their home. I had given specific parameters for the trip to Neoptolemus and Eunice, which had given them some assurance. But those assurances had not included where the Holy Spirit was leading us now!

Yet, we all knew this was the right thing to do. We were surprised to meet Luke on the streets of Troas not long after we arrived. "Shortly after the two of you left Antioch," he told us, "the Spirit of the Lord came to me in a dream and told me to come to Troas. I asked Him, 'For what purpose?' He responded, 'I will show you once you get there.'

"I questioned whether or not it was really the Lord. But when He directed me a second time, I knew I must make haste. I set off on my journey and arrived this morning. Now that I have encountered the two of you, I know God's purpose must involve you. So, I remain His servant – and yours – and will await His next instruction!"

That night, I had a vision. I saw a man from Macedonia pleading with me, saying, "*Come over here and help us.*"(5) The next morning, I shared my dream with Silas, Luke, and Timothy. There was no question what God was directing us to do next!

We boarded a boat that day and sailed to the island of Samothrace. After spending the night there, we sailed on to the harbor of Neapolis, arriving the next day. God had brought us to Macedonia … now we would see what He had planned!

* * *

23

On the Sabbath we went a little way outside the city to a riverbank, where we thought people would be meeting for prayer, and we sat down to speak with some women who had gathered there.[1]

* * *

We knew when we sailed into the harbor at Neapolis we had crossed into a different region of the world. It was unlike anywhere else I had ever been. The port and surrounding towns had originally been established by the Macedons in the 4th century B.C. for the mining of gold from the region. Soldiers had been assigned to several garrisons to protect the mining operations. One of those garrisons, situated sixteen kilometers inland from Neapolis, was the town of Philippi, named in honor of their King Philip II, the father of Alexander the Great. For 200 years, it served in that capacity as a strategic military outpost.

But that all changed when the region came under Roman rule. One of Rome's massive accomplishments in the 2nd century B.C. was the construction of the Via Egnatia, a highway built on the backs of slave labor, that stretched almost 800 kilometers from the Adriatic Sea to the Aegean Sea. It created an efficient trade route on which to move soldiers and goods over land from Italy to Asia and back again.

Located at its eastern end, Philippi became a strategic center – politically, commercially, militarily, and culturally. The city was redeveloped using a pattern similar to that of Rome and was colonized by veteran soldiers, many of whom were from the elite Praetorian guard. Other Roman citizens who were seeking opportunity and gain as the empire expanded also flocked to the city, and its borders eventually extended to Neapolis. Two military officers were appointed to be the duumviri – the co-magistrates who governed the city.

The day after our arrival was the Sabbath. As usual, we headed to the local synagogue — but we quickly discovered there wasn't one. Jewish custom requires there be at least ten men for the establishment of a synagogue, so apparently there were not ten Jewish men living in the city. However, we did learn there was a group of women who gathered for prayer on the Sabbath along the riverbank. It seemed my call to come to Macedonia through the vision of a man was actually God's response to the prayers of a gathering of women!

As we spoke with the women, I learned that one named Lydia was a successful merchant from Thyatira. She was a freeborn single woman who sold purple cloth. She had recently moved to Philippi to ply her trade. Her native city of Thyatira in Asia was the trade center for indigo dyes. It was one of the cities the Holy Spirit had recently prevented Silas, Timothy, and me from entering.

It soon became obvious God was already at work drawing these women to Himself. Lydia shared that she had already turned from the paganism in which she had been raised and was seeking the one true God – even though she had not yet heard the Good News of Jesus. She was a testimony that those who honestly seek to know God will find Him. The words of Moses rang true through Lydia's life: "*If from there you seek the Lord your*

God, you will find Him if you seek Him with all your heart and with all your soul."[2]

As we shared the Gospel, the Lord opened Lydia's heart and she believed. We then baptized her, along with her servants who had also believed. After her baptism, she invited us to be guests in her home. She said, *"If you agree that I am faithful to the Lord, come and stay at my home."*[3] Soon her home became more than our place of lodging, it became the meeting place for that new church.

Not surprisingly, the movement of the Holy Spirit at the riverbank was quickly followed by an attack of the evil one. He did not like us invading his territory. In the days immediately following, we encountered a slave girl who was possessed by a demon. She earned money for her masters by telling fortunes. She began to follow us each day, shouting, *"These men are servants of the Most High God, and they have come to tell you how to be saved."*[4]

One day, I became so exasperated that I turned and commanded the demon, *"I command you in the name of Jesus Christ to come out of her!"*[5] Instantly it left her – and with it, her ability to tell fortunes and earn money for her masters. They grabbed Silas and me and dragged us before the authorities in the center of the forum shouting, *"The whole city is in an uproar because of these Jews. They are teaching customs that are illegal for us Romans to practice."*[5]

A mob soon formed around us. In light of their own religious and racial prejudices, the duumviri ordered that Silas and I be stripped and beaten. The fact we were Roman citizens should have prevented this, but they failed to investigate the matter fully. Instead, they ordered the jailer to severely beat us with wooden rods and then lock us in prison. The jailer took no chances. He locked us in the inner dungeon and clamped our feet in stocks.

. . .

We were wrongfully accused, wrongfully judged, and wrongfully punished. But as we sat in that dungeon, an overwhelming peace came over us – a peace that could only be explained by the presence of the Holy Spirit. Our heads told us we should shout at the top of our lungs with pleas of innocence and injustice, but our spirits told us to lift our voices to God with praises and hymns.

Around midnight, as the other prisoners were listening to us praying and singing, a great earthquake shook the very foundation of the prison. All the doors flew open, and the chains of every prisoner fell off. Although the prisoners could have fled to freedom, they remained right where they were. They sat there in awe of God, which overshadowed any fear they had of our Roman captors. I don't know with complete certainty, but I believe a number of our fellow prisoners came to faith in Jesus that night.

My attention was fixed on the jailer – one for whom Christ had placed us in the prison. Roman law demands that if a jailer loses a prisoner, he will receive the same punishment as the prisoner. Several of the men imprisoned with us were facing severe punishments. When the jailer saw the doors were open and feared the prisoners had escaped, he knew the penalty he would face. I watched as he drew his sword to kill himself.

It would have been easy to justify taking vengeance on our persecutor by allowing him to take his own life. But I knew the jailer was really the prisoner – imprisoned by his own sin. Silas and I were truly freed men – set free from the bondage of sin. I knew I was no more worthy of the grace extended to me through the compassion of Christ than this cruel jailer. So, I shouted out, *"Don't kill yourself! We are all here!"*[7]

The power of God is what had seized the jailer's attention, but it was the grace and compassion of God that made him realize his need for a Savior. It wasn't the supernatural power of the earthquake that God used to draw this man to Himself; it was a spirit of humility, grace, and kindness that drew him to the Gospel.

• • •

Trembling with fear, he asked, *"Sirs, what must I do to be saved?"*(8) That night, he and all the members of his household heard the Good News, believed, and were baptized. An evening that started with the jailer subjecting us to severe beatings ended with him washing our wounds and extending us hospitality.

The next morning the duumviri sent soldiers to tell the jailer, *"Let those men go!"*(9) So the jailer told me, *"The city officials have said you and Silas are free to leave. Go in peace."*(10)

But I replied, *"They have publicly beaten us without a trial and put us in prison – and we are Roman citizens. So now they want us to leave secretly? Certainly not! Let them come themselves to release us!"*(11)

When the soldiers reported back to them, the duumviri became frightened when they learned we were Roman citizens – they knew what could happen to them. So they came to the jail and apologized to us. After they had personally escorted us out of jail, they begged us to leave the city.

We told them we would leave after we attended to some matters in the city. The duumviri nervously watched as we walked to Lydia's home. There we met with her and the other believers and encouraged them. The household of Lydia, combined with the household of the jailer, had now formed the core of a budding new church. I asked Luke to remain with them to train up leaders. Then Silas, Timothy, and I left town.

We traveled to Thessalonica, a city named after the stepsister of Alexander the Great, and one that had become another prominent city in the region. Three rivers flowed from the city into the Aegean Sea, which made it another major seaport for trade and transportation. It was a "free city," which meant it had an elected citizens' assembly, and it had no Roman garrison stationed within its walls.

. . .

We knew there were more than ten Jewish men in Thessalonica because there was a synagogue in the city. I labored in my tentmaking trade throughout the week, but on the Sabbath day I went to the synagogue looking for devout Jews, as well as Gentiles, God-seekers, and new believers. I returned for two more Sabbaths, each time using the Scriptures to point to the Gospel message.

After three weeks of ministry, we saw a large number of people believe, especially Greek proselytes and a group of women of influence. Among the men were Aristarchus and Secundus, as well as Jason, who had welcomed us to lodge in his home. But seeing the response of the people to the Gospel, the unbelieving Jews became envious, formed a mob, and began to incite a riot against this infant church. They declared, *"These men who have turned the world upside down have come here also."*(12)

The Jews wanted to bring us before the city council under false accusations. Unable to find us, they turned to Jason, Aristarchus, and some of the other new local believers and brought them before the council instead. They declared them to be guilty of treason by virtue of their newly professed faith in Jesus. These believers were now themselves being accused of "turning the world upside down."

But as Aristarchus explained at the very beginning of this story, the crowd had lost sight that the politarch who was hearing their charges was, in fact, Aristarchus's father. Even he became a believer later that night, but to bring peace to the city, he required Jason and Aristarchus to post a bond and guarantee we would leave the city and not return. This was Satan's attempt through the unbelieving Jews to hinder the work the Spirit of God had begun in this city. But though *we* would be forced to leave, they soon discovered that what God begins, He continues and brings to completion.

As I later wrote to the believers in Thessalonica:

"You received the message with joy from the Holy Spirit in spite of the severe suffering

it brought you. In this way, you imitated both us and the Lord. As a result, you have become an example to all the believers in Greece – throughout both Macedonia and Achaia. And now the word of the Lord is ringing out from you to people everywhere, even beyond Macedonia and Achaia, for wherever we go we find people telling us about your faith in God. We don't need to tell them about it, for they keep talking about the wonderful welcome you gave us and how you turned away from idols to serve the living and true God. And they speak of how you are looking forward to the coming of God's Son from heaven – Jesus, whom God raised from the dead."(13)

After leaving Thessalonica, we preached the Gospel in the city of Berea. The Jews in Thessalonica soon heard the news and traveled to Berea to disrupt our work. Still, there were many who believed in Jesus. But the new believers, sensing the danger I was in, encouraged me to leave the city. Some of the believers traveled with me as I departed from Berea and went to Athens, while Silas and Timothy remained in Berea to disciple the new believers.

While waiting for Silas and Timothy to rejoin me, I went to the synagogue on the Sabbath. I spent the remaining days of the week in the public square, repairing tents and sharing the Good News of Jesus. As I walked through the city, I noticed their many objects of worship. I saw their altars, their idols, and their temples. As a matter of fact, they even had an altar to the "Unknown God." The Athenians didn't want to leave anyone out. Everything and anything had become the object of their worship – except the one true God.

Before long, the Epicurean and Stoic philosophers began to debate me. It reminded me of my debates with my childhood friend Ashmus. Sadly, our last debate had ended with him rejecting the Gospel – just as these men were doing as they shouted, *"This babbler has picked up some strange ideas. He's pushing some foreign religion."*(14)

The crowd assembling around us demanded I be taken to the rock called Mars Hill – which was named after the Roman god of war. Overlooking the city marketplace, the rock was the location where the council of judges would deliberate over crimes, disputes, and matters of religion. Once we got there, the crowd insisted I make my case before the council.

"*Men of Athens,*" I began, "*I notice that you are very religious in every way, for as I was walking along, I saw your many shrines. And one of your altars had this inscription on it: 'To an Unknown God.' This God, whom you worship without knowing, is the One I'm telling you about. He is the God who made the world and everything in it. From one man He created all the nations throughout the whole earth.*

"*His purpose was for the nations to seek after Him and perhaps feel their way toward Him and find Him – though He is not far from any one of us. He commands everyone everywhere to repent of their sins and turn to Him. For He has set a day for judging the world with justice by the Man He has appointed, and He proved to everyone who this is by raising Him from the dead.*"(15)

When I spoke about the resurrection of the dead, some began to laugh in contempt, but others said, "*We want to hear more about this later.*"(16) Several followed me as I left that place, including one of the judges and his wife.

The judge's name was Dionysius, and his wife's name was Damaris. They invited me to come to their home because he still had many questions. As our conversation unfolded, he told me, "Twenty-two years ago when I was still a lad, I traveled with my father to the courts of Cairo. A dispute had arisen between a prominent Athenian ship owner and an equally prominent Egyptian merchant. Both men had powerful friends in Rome, whom they convinced to come to their aid in the settlement of their dispute.

"My father was dispatched from Athens to assist in adjudicating a settlement of the matter. I was delighted when he chose to take me with him. We sailed by ship to Alexandria and from there traveled down the Nile River to Cairo. Both cities, though strikingly different from Athens, were beautiful, and I marveled at the majestic sight of the pyramids and the great halls.

. . .

"One of the days we were there, the sky suddenly turned dark at midday and stayed that way for three hours. It was a Friday. I remember the day as if it were yesterday. I remember thinking the gods were suffering at that moment and the god over them all must be experiencing great pain. No one could give me an explanation – not my father nor any of the priests I questioned upon our return to Athens.

"That day has remained a mystery to me until today." Then he asked me, "When was this Man Jesus whom you speak of crucified on the cross?"

I answered, "It was on a Friday … twenty-two years ago. Then three days later He arose from the grave."

Dionysius turned to his wife and then looked at me before raising his gaze and exclaiming heavenward, "You are the One whom I have been seeking for these twenty-two years. I have been worshiping You, though I have not known Your name. Today, I know Your name. You are Jesus, the Son of the Living God! From this day forward I will follow You!"

Later that day I baptized Dionysius, Damaris, and other members of their household as they became the first believers in Athens. In the following weeks, others came to faith in Jesus as well. I taught them in the Scriptures and entrusted them to the Spirit of the Lord.

There would always be more work to be done in Athens. But God was giving those assignments to others, including Dionysius and Damaris. My part was complete, and now the Spirit was leading me to Corinth.

* * *

24

Then Paul left Athens and went to Corinth.[1]

* * *

Corinth's reputation for wickedness was well-known throughout the Roman empire. With a population of 200,000 people, the city was the capital of the province of Achaia and a center for trade – of all types – and travel. Money, vice, and philosophies of all varieties found a home in Corinth. There were countless philosophers and teachers of false religions there who preyed on and easily swayed a superstitious population. When people live in a city built on the fulfillment of feelings and desires instead of truth, they will fall for anything – because they stand for nothing.

I distinguished myself from the plethora of religious hucksters in the city by supporting myself as a tentmaker. Soon after I arrived, I met another tentmaker named Aquila who had recently arrived from Italy with his wife, Priscilla. They had left Rome when Caesar Claudius ordered the expulsion of all Jews from the city. I met them on my first Sabbath day in the city while attending the synagogue. They were the first people to believe and be baptized in the city.

. . .

They immediately became co-laborers with me – not only in plying our tentmaking trade but also in spreading the Gospel throughout the city. With their hands, hearts, and home, they dedicated themselves to the work of the Lord. When Silas and Timothy arrived from Berea and Thessalonica, they brought with them financial aid from the church in Philippi, which enabled me to spend more of my time preaching.

Many Jews in the city opposed and insulted me. One notable exception was Crispus, the leader of the synagogue. Together with everyone in his household, Crispus came to believe in Christ and became part of the new church in Corinth. The rejection of the Gospel by the Jews was a release from God for me to preach among the Gentiles.

The Spirit of the Lord led me to a new Gentile proselyte named Titius Justus. He was a person of peace who soon also believed in Jesus and opened his home for the new followers to gather for worship and the teaching of the Good News. Titius Justus lived right next door to the synagogue, so the Jews could easily see how many were coming to faith and being baptized. Though Jewish opposition grew, God did not lead me to leave Corinth as He had in Thessalonica and Berea. Rather, He encouraged me to stand firm and remain faithful in that which He had placed before me, saying: *"For I am with you, and no one will attack and harm you, for many people in this city belong to Me."*(2)

I remained in the city for the next eighteen months – not only confident in the promise of God but also in the presence of His Spirit.

Several months into my stay, Rome dispatched a new governor to the city named Gallio. His arrival gave the unbelieving Jews hope Rome might declare this new "Christian sect" illegal. Under the direction of the new leader of the synagogue, Sosthenes, they illegally assembled a mob and forcefully brought me before Gallio, making false accusations against me, saying, *"He is persuading people to worship God in ways that are contrary to our law."*(3)

• • •

But even before I was able to defend myself, Gallio turned to my accusers and said, "*Listen, you Jews, if this were a case involving some wrongdoing or a serious crime, I would have a reason to accept your case. But since it is merely a question of words and names and your Jewish law, take care of it yourselves. I refuse to judge such matters.*"(4)

He then directed them to leave his courtroom. I never was required to defend myself – my Defender had raised up the governor to come to my defense! The crowd then turned on Sosthenes, who had brought the charges, and they beat him there in the courtroom.

I was all too familiar with receiving beatings like that. So, after the crowd left, the other believers and I ministered to his injuries. God truly does work in mysterious ways – and in ways we would never anticipate – or even ask or think. Because of our compassion toward Sosthenes, he came to a saving relationship with Jesus. Sosthenes became not only a brother in Christ but also a trusted co-laborer with me.

We stayed in Corinth for several more months until the day the Spirit directed me to leave. We knew Silas was to remain there teaching the believers, while I returned to Jerusalem and Antioch to report on all we had seen God accomplish. Timothy and I bid farewell to Silas, Sosthenes, and the other brothers and sisters, and set sail for the port of Ephesus, taking Aquila and Priscilla with us.

The port of Corinth was situated in the seaside town of Cenchrea on the eastern side of the main city. As I prepared to board the ship for the voyage to Ephesus, I was overwhelmed with thanksgiving to God for the way He had ordered our steps these past three years since we left Antioch. I planned to travel to Jerusalem to bring a report to the apostles and elders there before returning to Antioch. It would take me about three weeks to get to Jerusalem. I suddenly felt impressed by the Spirit to take the vow of a Nazirite, symbolizing my separation and devotion to God as an expression of thanksgiving to Him.

. . .

In keeping with the practice surrounding such a vow, I left my companions at the ship and went off alone. I shaved my head and placed my shorn hair into a container to be presented as an offering at the temple in Jerusalem. Until that day, I would not drink anything produced from the vine, nor would I eat any food regarded as unclean. I was not doing so to gain God's favor or garner the attention of people. Neither was I doing it to elevate the Jewish laws regarding food over the practices of my Gentile brothers. Rather, I was fasting from food and drink as an expression of my love, devotion, and thanksgiving to God alone. Having entered into the vow, I returned and boarded the ship with the others for our two-day voyage across the Aegean Sea to Ephesus.

By the time we docked at our destination, the captain of our ship and two members of his crew were brothers in Christ. We celebrated their new life through baptism along the shore before we said goodbye to Timothy. He was leaving to journey home to Lystra. The rest of us were scheduled to remain in port for two days while the captain traded the goods he had brought from Athens for those he intended to pick up in Ephesus. Again, I decided to leave the others behind at the dock as I made my way to the local synagogue.

Those gathered at the synagogue saw my shaved head and asked why I had taken such a vow. It gave me the opportunity to share the Good News with them. Some of the men began to debate me; others earnestly asked me questions. I remained overnight to answer their questions. By the next day, several had become believers. Although they asked me to stay a while, I knew I must go.

It was then the Holy Spirit prompted me that Aquila and Priscilla should remain in Ephesus to teach the new believers and preach the Good News. The next day, I continued the voyage to Caesarea Maritima alone, where we arrived six days later.

It took me four days to journey by foot to Jerusalem. I arrived on the eve of the celebration of the Feast of Tabernacles. The feast commemorates the years the Jews spent in the desert on their way to the Promised Land. The city was filled with pilgrims who had come for the celebration. The area surrounding the city was packed with open-air huts with roofs of branches and leaves. Those attending the festival had erected the huts as a reminder of the temporary housing the Israelites used as they journeyed through the wilderness.

For those who have not accepted Jesus as Messiah, the feast is a time to remember God's provision to His people throughout those forty years. For those of us who believe in Jesus and have trusted Him by faith, it is a time when we look forward to when Jesus will return to establish His throne. It is a time of great joy! It was fitting that the period of my Nazirite vow would conclude on the eve of this important celebration.

I made my way to the temple and presented my shorn hair, together with a peace offering, to the priest. He lifted the gifts up before the Lord in a gesture of offering and then placed them on the fire. I knew I no longer needed a human priest to be my intermediary before God. Jesus is the Priestly King and through Him every believer has been given access to the Father. But I believed God would have me present this offering as a Jew in the manner He had set forth through Moses. I had not come to the temple to present an offering since believing in Jesus, and I have not done so since. Jesus died on the cross as our everlasting sacrifice. But this was a unique offering of thanksgiving to God for what He had done through this particular journey.

While I was at the temple, I learned that the current high priest, Ananias (son of Nedebeus) had been accused by Quadratus, the current governor of the region, with inciting violence against Rome. He had been taken to Rome where he was awaiting trial. His arrest had only served to increase the animosity of the Jews toward the Romans. The tension in the city was palpable.

After I completed my time at the temple, I went to the home of Mnason and together we looked for the rest of the elders and apostles of the church. James greeted me affectionately as did the apostles John, Simon (often called the Zealot), James (the son of Clopas), and Matthias. They told me Peter had been in Rome for slightly less than two years preaching the Good News. The other apostles had scattered as well. Andrew had traveled to the cities around the Black Sea. Philip was in Phrygia. Bartholomew was traveling throughout the Indo-Parthian kingdom. Thomas and Matthew were separately preaching among the Parthians, Medes, and Persians. Thaddeus had gone to Mesopotamia.

They also told me the Jews' persecution of believers in Jerusalem had somewhat subsided. They were now focused on directing their hatred toward the Romans, who in turn gave the Jews little rein to carry out violence on anyone else. Many eyes were watching the outcome of the high priest's trial in Rome. It would set the tone for Roman-Jewish relations for years to come.

I relayed to the church leaders what the Spirit of the Lord had done throughout my travels, as well as the enthusiastic response from the Gentile believers to the message these elders had sent them. We rejoiced in how the Lord was building His church and how the Good News of the Gospel was spreading across the land.

I remained in Jerusalem with Mnason for two more weeks and then departed for Antioch, where I stayed through the winter and into early spring. I received news the Roman emperor, Claudius, had died, and his adopted son, Nero, had succeeded him. It was too early to know how this change would affect the persecution of the church under Jewish hands or Roman hands. I also found out the high priest, Ananias, had been sent back to Jerusalem without receiving any punishment.

However, soon after his return, violence erupted in Caesarea over a local ordinance that restricted the civil rights of Jews. The Roman garrison was dispatched to charge the Jewish dissidents who were armed with clubs and swords. When news of the skirmish reached Rome, Nero was outraged by what he considered an attack on his leadership. The rights of

Jews were further restricted throughout the Iudaean province. The question remained what impact this would have on Jews living throughout the remainder of the empire, including those who were now Jewish Christians. I reminded the brothers and sisters in Antioch that we are citizens of heaven where the Lord Jesus Christ reigns. We must remain steadfast in His mission until the day He returns.

The Lord soon showed me it was time to return to Galatia and Phrygia. The elders of the church prayed over me and sent me out with financial resources and prayer support I knew would never be exhausted.

I was able to spend a few days with my family in Tarsus. It had been four years since I had last seen them. My nephew, Hezron, was now twenty-two years old. I was struck by his maturity – his care and concern for his family, the character he exemplified, and the spiritual maturity present in his words and actions.

My sister, Dinah, asked if I would consider taking him with me on this journey. I knew without question the Spirit was leading me to do so. It would be a sacrifice for my brother-in-law, Reuben, and Dinah to send him off. They had grown to depend on him greatly in their tentmaking business. But they did so knowing it was God's plan for Hezron – and for them.

Hezron had also become a key leader in the church, and his absence would be felt there as well. The church in Tarsus would be sending out one of their best. But to their credit, they told me they would only give God their best. Reuben and the other church elders told me they knew that as they released their best to God, He would raise up others. "Brother Paul," they said, "you have told us we can't outgive God. If we give, it will be given to us – good measure, pressed down, shaken together, and running over. That's not only true as it relates to our money; it's also true as it relates to our sons and daughters and all He has entrusted to us."

. . .

One week later, Hezron and I set out together. We stopped in Derbe for a few weeks to encourage the believers there. Next, we traveled to Lystra. When we arrived at the home of Neoptolemus, I was overjoyed to be reunited with Timothy and the entire family and to hear how the Spirit of the Lord was continuing to move across the city. The church was flourishing! Jews and Gentiles alike were coming to faith, and the city itself was changing as a result.

Late that first afternoon, a man arrived at their door. He looked familiar to me, but I could not recall who he was. Neoptolemus introduced him to me saying, "Paul, this is our brother, Abram. He recently became a follower of Jesus. He heard you had arrived today, and he has come to see you in earnest."

"Welcome, brother Abram," I said. "I rejoice that you have believed and become a part of the family of God! What brings you to seek me out?"

"I have prayed for months," he replied, "asking God to grant me this day to stand before you. I know God has forgiven me, but I have come seeking your forgiveness as well."

"What have you done that requires my forgiveness?" I asked.

Abram remained silent, and as he looked at me his eyes began to fill with tears. After a few moments, he began. "Because I am one of the men who dragged you to the edge of the city. I hurled false accusations and insults at you. I said all manner of evil against you – and then I was one of the men who threw stones at you. With anger and hatred in my heart, I left you in a heap on the ground, believing you to be dead. By God's grace you survived, but that in no way lessens my guilt … or my shame."

Abram sobbed as he continued. "For more than five years, I struggled under the weight of my guilt, though I attempted to justify my actions as being righteous. I contended that you were preaching heresy and I was required to do what I did to defend the laws of God. But all the time I knew what I had done was wrong – and a voice inside me kept telling me you had spoken the truth.

"One day a few weeks ago, I heard Timothy preaching the Good News – and I knew it was true. It was as if the barrier I had erected in my heart and mind to keep me from accepting the truth shattered, and God's forgiveness flooded over me. My sins were washed away by the blood of Jesus. I knew I was a new creation. The burden of guilt was lifted off me – not only for what I had done to you, but for all of my sins … and they were many.

"From that moment on, I began to ask God to grant me the opportunity to see you and seek your forgiveness. There is nothing I can say or do to adequately express my sorrow over what I did to you. And if you were to withhold your forgiveness, you would be well within your right. For it has only been by grace I have been saved, and it would also only be by grace if you were to forgive me."

I looked at this broken man who was now kneeling before me, and I, too, began to sob. I knelt before Him and placed my arm around his neck, saying, "My brother, Jesus came into this world to save sinners, and I am chief among them. Whatever you have done, I have done far worse. And yet, God by His everlasting grace and mercy has forgiven me. His forgiveness of me is far greater than anything I could ever extend to you. I forgive you – and I rejoice in knowing we are now both bondservants together to our Lord and Savior, Jesus the Messiah!" Together we lifted our voices in praise and thanksgiving to God into the night.

Hezron and I remained in Lystra as I taught the believers and preached the Gospel for a month before the Spirit showed me it was time to move on. I was pleased to have Timothy join us as we made our way across Phrygia and Asia toward the city of Ephesus.

25

Paul traveled through the interior provinces. Finally, he came to Ephesus, where he found several believers.[1]

* * *

When we arrived in Ephesus, we immediately sought out Priscilla and Aquila. It had been about a year since I had left them there.

Ephesus, with its 300,000 inhabitants, is the capital of the Roman province of Asia and serves as an important commercial center, thanks to its thriving harbor. The city also attracts hosts of visitors to the temple of Diana, considered one of the seven wonders of the Roman world. Cultic prostitution is an important part of its temple worship, and hundreds of "priestesses" make themselves available in the temple.

Priscilla and Aquila updated me on everything that had happened since I last saw them. They told me about an evangelist named Apollos who had arrived in the city soon after I left. He had been well schooled in the Scriptures in Alexandria and was a bold, confident, and eloquent preacher. The only problem was he had not heard the whole Gospel.

. . .

While he was receiving his education, he had learned the truths that John the baptizer had proclaimed. John had preached about salvation that was soon to come through the Messiah. He had even preached about a future baptism of the Holy Spirit. But neither of those two prophecies had been fulfilled at the time John was beheaded. He had believed by faith but never witnessed it by sight – and at the time, neither had his disciples. So, the message Apollos had heard and believed in Alexandria stopped short of the Good News of the death, burial, and resurrection of Jesus. Apollos had not yet believed in Jesus because he had not heard about His redemptive work!

Consequently, he had come to Ephesus preaching a message of repentance, but not salvation, and had baptized those who repented with the baptism of John. God sovereignly arranged for Apollos to encounter Priscilla and Aquilla while he was in Ephesus so he could hear the way of God more accurately and more completely. As a result, Apollos came to faith and truly believed and was himself then baptized.

A few months later, Priscilla and Aquila, along with the other believers in Ephesus, were led by the Holy Spirit to send Apollos to Corinth. By then Silas had left Corinth, and Apollos's understanding of the Scriptures would be a great help in nurturing that young church. Apollos had departed for Corinth a few weeks before my return to Ephesus.

A few days after I arrived, I encountered twelve men who had been discipled by Apollos before he himself had trusted in Jesus. When the men told me they had not yet heard of the Holy Spirit, I knew they were not yet truly born again. They had been baptized and were seeking to be religious, but they did not know the complete Gospel of the saving work of Jesus. Therefore, they had not yet had an opportunity to fully receive the free gift of salvation.

. . .

I explained to the twelve that a person's baptismal experience was a clear indication of his or her spiritual condition and understanding. There were those like them who had been baptized with the baptism of John, which is a baptism of repentance under the Old Covenant, looking forward to the arrival of the coming Messiah. It was important before the arrival of Jesus because it acknowledged our need for a Savior and the promise of His coming.

Once Jesus began His earthly ministry, the baptism being performed by His disciples confirmed the arrival of the Messiah, but it still looked ahead to His death, burial. and resurrection, to be followed by the arrival of the Holy Spirit. Then there was the baptism that began on and following the Day of Pentecost, acknowledging the completed work of salvation through Christ and the indwelling presence of His Holy Spirit. That is the Good News we have come to preach:

- sinners hear the Word of God
- they repent of their sin and believe in Jesus Christ
- they immediately receive the Holy Spirit
- they are baptized as a testimony of their salvation.

"There can be no salvation apart from the saving work of Jesus through His death, burial, and resurrection," I told them. "Then once we repent and believe by faith in Jesus, He seals our salvation by living within us with His Spirit. We follow Christ in water baptism as an act of obedience, bearing public testimony of the salvation we have received by grace."

After I shared the Good News with these twelve men, they all believed and were baptized. I used this opportunity to teach Timothy and Hezron. "It isn't sufficient for us to be passionate and bold," I told them, "and yet only declare a portion of the Gospel as Apollos has done. In his lack of knowledge, he had enthusiastically led these twelve men to have only partial understanding – a partial understanding that still left them without a saving relationship with Jesus. Left in that condition, these men would have, in turn, passed that *fatal* flaw – that incomplete truth – on to others. Do not use lofty words and impressive wisdom to tell God's secret plan.

Forget everything except Jesus Christ, the One who was crucified. Rather than using clever and persuasive speeches, rely only on the power of the Holy Spirit, so those to whom you are speaking will trust not in human wisdom but in the power of God."

For my next three months in Ephesus, I preached boldly in the synagogue – where some believed but others did not. Those who did not began to openly oppose me, so I began looking for another location. A few weeks prior, Aquila had introduced me to Tyrannus, the headmaster of a school in the heart of the city. He was very proud of his school and had explained to me in detail how the school operated. Classes met each morning until an hour before midday and then resumed five hours later. That meant the lecture hall was not used those five hours each day. When I asked if I could use his hall to teach during those hours, he replied, "My hope is to see the mind and soul stretched by stimulating thought. I find your teachings about this Man Jesus to be very stimulating – so yes, you are welcome to teach in my lecture hall."

For the next two years, the lecture hall was filled each day as people from throughout the province of Asia – both Jews and Gentiles – heard the Lord's message. As I spoke, God evidenced His anointing on my life by giving me the power to do unusual miracles. The sick were even healed when handkerchiefs or cloths that had touched my skin were placed on them, and any evil spirits within them were driven out.

There was a Jewish priest named Sceva who had seven sons. When he heard about the miracles God was accomplishing through me, he saw an opportunity to profit. He sent out his sons with the instructions to cast out evil spirits using the incantation:

"I command you by Jesus, whom Paul preaches, to come out!"[2]

But when they tried it on a man possessed by an evil spirit, the spirit replied, *"I know Jesus, and I know Paul. But who are you?"*[3] Then the evil spirit leapt on them with such violence they fled from the house naked and badly injured.

. . .

The story of what happened quickly spread throughout Ephesus and a solemn fear came over the city; then the name of Jesus was greatly revered and praised. Many became believers and repented from their sinful practices. A number who had been practicing magic brought their incantation books and burned them at a public bonfire.

About that time, Aristarchus and Gaius arrived in Ephesus from Corinth, accompanied by Sosthenes. They reported distressing news about the church in Corinth, which was struggling with issues of immorality and factions that had developed among the believers. The observance of the Lord's Supper was becoming a drunken feast and spiritual gifts were being used for selfish purposes. It prompted me to dispatch Timothy to Corinth – with his pastoral heart – to deliver a letter of chastisement and correction that Sosthenes helped me write.

A few months later, Timothy returned expressing further concerns he had about the Corinthian church, which included a significant personal offense against me and a challenge to my authority by one specific individual. One bright spot about Timothy's return was he brought Erastus with him.

Erastus was the city treasurer in Corinth and a new believer in Jesus. His position in the city gave him great influence. His duties included the upkeep of civic buildings, city streets, and city services, as well as the collection of public revenue. In that role, he was frequently called upon to settle public disputes. He had come to faith during my second trip to Corinth and was now a leader in the church. Timothy had brought him back to bear further witness of the continuing turmoil in Corinth.

Despite his prominent rank in the city government, Erastus regarded ministry as his top priority. He left his work in Corinth to ask me to help bring healing to the division in the church. Though I was heartbroken to hear his news, I was encouraged by the faith and testimony of Erastus. I decided to send Priscilla, Aquila, and Sosthenes back to Corinth, and I kept Timothy and Erastus with me.

It was soon thereafter when I felt the Holy Spirit prompting me to return to Jerusalem, even though there was still much work to be done in Ephesus. He instructed me to first spend some time with the churches in Macedonia, Greece, and Asia. I sent Timothy and Erastus on ahead to Macedonia while I completed my work in Ephesus.

I continued teaching each day and sending out those who were coming to Christ to do likewise throughout the city. And the Holy Spirit was drawing more and more to faith each day.

There were many craftsmen and sellers who had over time gotten very wealthy from the rampant idolatry and immorality surrounding the worship of Diana. Now that many in the city were coming to faith in Christ, those craftsmen and sellers were beginning to see a significant decline in their income. One craftsman in particular, named Demetrius, and the silversmiths he employed were more concerned for their jobs and declining incomes than they were about any truth regarding Diana and the temple. But they were cunning enough to not make their personal interests known; rather, they chose to use the art of manipulation. Demetrius made use of the two things Ephesians treasured the most – the honor of their city and their perceived greatness of the goddess and her temple.

He was able to use those two passions to stir many in the city into an uproar – which quickly grew into a riot. A crowd of about 25,000 people, shouting and frenzied, began to make their way through the streets to the amphitheater. They intended to seize me en route, but when they arrived at the lecture hall I was not there. Instead, they seized two of my companions, Gaius and Aristarchus.

By this point, Aristarchus was almost used to being seized by a mob and taken before a magistrate – but this time the magistrate wasn't his father.

When I learned what had taken place, I headed to the amphitheater to stand with Gaius and Aristarchus. But several of the church elders, as well as some of the city officials, told me my presence would only aggravate the situation. They wisely counseled me to stay away.

Most of the people at the amphitheater had no idea what was happening. They had been caught up in the emotion of the moment – and there is nothing more dangerous than an emotionally charged, disoriented crowd.

Prior to the riot, the Jewish leaders had become increasingly envious of the growing popularity of The Way. They were losing adherents at a troubling rate which was, in turn, diminishing their bases of power and income. The leaders apparently saw this riot as an opportunity to regain an upper hand. They pushed one of the leading members of the synagogue – a man named Alexander – forward to speak to the crowd. He too was a metal worker in the city, like Demetrius. The Jewish leaders must have thought the crowd would listen to Alexander since he was one of them. No doubt their plan was for him to tell the crowd the Jews did not endorse me or The Way, and they too wanted to stop the disruption that we were causing in the city.

But the crowd knew Jews did not approve of their idols or their worship of Diana. The Ephesians had always seen the Jews as interlopers into their way of life, as much if not more than followers of The Way. The only thing protecting the Jews to this point had been Roman law that gave them freedom of religion. But that protection didn't appear to matter to this crowd. Alexander's appearance only antagonized them further, causing their deafening shouts to drown him out for more than two hours.

Finally, it was the mayor who was able to quiet the crowd – and the mayor's interruption was motivated politically for his own self-preservation. Ephesus had been designated as a "free city" by Rome with its own elected citizens' assembly. Rome extended that privilege merely as a concession and would have welcomed any excuse to revoke that benefit. If Rome chose to do so, the mayor would be out of a job. So, he used the same tactics to calm the crowd that Demetrius had employed to arouse them. He reminded them of the greatness of their city and of their goddess.

He declared that all the members of The Way, including me, were innocent of any crime. Rather, he accused Demetrius and the craftsmen of acting in an unlawful manner and admonished them to seek lawful remedy if they truly had any valid complaints.

The crowd chose to heed the mayor's direction and calmly returned to their homes, congratulating themselves for their success in defending their great city and their famous goddess. Regrettably, however, the event did not appear to cause any of the rioters to question the truthfulness of their beliefs or the truths of the Gospel. As is often the case, it is easier to believe a lie and follow the crowd than to take a stand for the truth.

The riot demonstrated that my continuing presence, together with that of Aristarchus and Gaius, would serve to further inflame the city. The elders were now well-equipped to lead the church. So I sent for the believers, encouraged them, told them goodbye, and departed for Macedonia.

During the next several weeks, God brought a unique group of men to travel with me. They were Gentiles and Jews from Judea, Syria, Cilicia, Asia, Macedonia, and Achaia. They were public officials, commoners, aristocrats, and slaves who represented a diversity of backgrounds, languages, and cultures. But they were all devoted followers of Jesus and obedient to His mission.

Our entourage traveled through Troas with the hope I would see Titus. After I led him to the Lord, Titus often served as my secretary and interpreter. He was one of the men who accompanied Barnabas and me to the council meeting in Jerusalem. Although I had encouraged the circumcision of Timothy, to render his ministry acceptable among the Jews, I never asked the same of Titus. I did not want to appear in agreement with those who required it of Gentile believers.

After Timothy and Erastus's report about the church in Corinth, I had sent another letter to the church a few weeks after I dispatched Aquila and Priscilla. Even though Aristarchus helped me write the letter, I knew it required a courier with a different gifting from his to deliver it. God led me to send Titus with the commission to strongly admonish the Corinthian saints. I was looking forward to hearing how the church had responded to my letter.

Trophimus was one of the Gentile believers from Ephesus. He had come to faith at the beginning of my time there, and I had witnessed the activity of God in his life throughout the three years we were together. I thought it would be a good opportunity for him to grow as a leader, so I instructed Trophimus to accompany Titus in carrying my letter to Corinth.

When we arrived in Troas, Titus and Trophimus had not yet returned, so I continued on to Macedonia to join Timothy and Erastus. Titus and Trophimus did finally catch up with us in Berea, and I was delighted by their report. The Corinthian church had responded with repentance, prompting me to write a third letter to them with the assistance of Timothy. Titus couriered that letter back to Corinth accompanied by a larger entourage. I told him I would join him in Corinth in three months and instructed him to organize a collection of alms from the Corinthian church for the Christians in Jerusalem. I was always able to count on Titus to get things done because of his gifting as a troubleshooter, a peacemaker, an organizer, and an evangelist.

Aristarchus continued to travel with me through Macedonia and Achaia and never once allowed himself to become discouraged by the trials and tribulations we had experienced in Ephesus.

• • •

Like Aristarchus, Secundus was another Gentile believer who had been raised in Thessalonica. But their city of birth was where any similarity between the two men stopped. While Aristarchus was from a wealthy and powerful family, Secundus was a slave. But they served the Lord side by side without ever giving it a second thought. This true friendship between a nobleman and a slave was viewed as scandalous by many in the Roman world; they found it hard to believe they could sit together and serve together in the church. Yet they did, because they believed who they were in Jesus Christ was more important than who they were thought to be in this world.

It was once said the ground is level at the foot of the cross. There is no one from such a high station of life they don't need Jesus. There is no one from such a low station of life that Jesus can't lift them up. All people must humble themselves and come through the same gate of faith to Jesus. It doesn't matter if you are an Aristarchus or a Secundus – Jesus is your only way, and so it is for everyone.

Two other Gentile brothers joined me on this trip. One was Sopater, a believer from Berea, who joined me in the city and traveled with us throughout Macedonia and Greece. The other was Tychicus, a native of Ephesus, who also had traveled to Corinth with Titus. He, too, had joined up with us in Berea. From the day I first met him, he reminded me of Barnabas. He is an encourager and extremely trustworthy. He is a brother who has often proved to us in many ways that he is zealous for the Gospel and a protective shepherd of the church.

Silas rejoined me while we were in Corinth. Three months had passed since I had been back in the city. Though I knew I needed to get to Jerusalem, I also knew I needed to invest time in the leaders of the church, strengthening and building them up. All my companions were a great help in nurturing the leaders.

Just as I was preparing to depart by ship for Antioch, Sopater and Silas came to tell me they had learned that a group of Jews knew about my travel plans and had plotted with the ship's captain to murder me on the voyage. Everyone agreed I must change my plans and travel by land through Macedonia to Philippi and then sail from Troas.

My companions and I set out that day on the journey and reunited with Luke in Philippi. I sent most of the others ahead to Troas while Silas, Luke, Hezron, and I remained in Philippi for five more days. We celebrated Passover and the remembrance of our Lord's death and resurrection with the Philippian church.

26

As soon as the Passover ended, we boarded a ship at Philippi and five days later arrived in Troas, where we stayed a week.[(1)]

* * *

On the first day of the following week, we gathered in an upper room in Troas to observe the Lord's Supper. Since I was scheduled to depart the next day, I preached until just before midnight. The room was lit with many flickering lamps, and everyone was seated wherever they could find a place.

A young man named Eutychus was sitting on a windowsill, drowsy from the soothing night air and the hypnotic effect of the flickering lights. He soon sank into a deep sleep and tumbled back, falling three stories through the open window.

I watched in horror as he disappeared from my sight. I sprinted down the stairs and was the first to arrive where he lay. Quickly, I determined he was not breathing and there were no signs of life. I wrapped my arms around him and cradled his broken body in my arms. Looking heavenward, I prayed, "Glorious Father of our Lord Jesus Christ, I ask that you restore this young man so that Your power over life and death is seen, and Your name and the name of Your Son are glorified."

Immediately the lad's eyes opened, and I called out to those who were standing around us, *"Don't worry, he's alive!"*[(2)] We praised God for His goodness and mercy as we watched Eutychus walk home with his parents by his side. I invited the rest of the people to rejoin me in the upper room, and I continued teaching them until dawn. After what we had just witnessed God do, no one else fell asleep!

Later, Silas told me he was concerned the Jews could still be plotting to kill me. He suggested Hezron and I travel to Assos on the other side of the peninsula by land. Silas and the rest of my travel companions would go ahead by ship to assess the danger. It would take both of us a day to make the journey.

Hezron and I actually arrived in Assos before the others, which gave me an opportunity to preach in the marketplace. Seeing the response of the people to the Gospel, I encouraged Timothy to remain in Assos so he could continue in the work that had now begun. The rest of us set sail for the three-day voyage to Miletus.

Ephesus is only a short distance from Miletus. Though my heart compelled me to return to Ephesus for a short while, I knew I could not. I knew I needed to be back in Jerusalem for the Festival of Pentecost, and that timeframe would not permit me to go to Ephesus. Instead, I sent Tychicus with a message for the elders of the church to come down to Miletus to meet with me.

When they arrived, I told them:

> *"You know that from the day I set foot in the province of Asia until now I have done the Lord's work humbly and with many tears. I have endured the trials that*

came to me from the plots of the Jews. I never shrank back from telling you what you needed to hear, either publicly or in your homes.

"And now I am bound by the Spirit to go to Jerusalem. I don't know what awaits me, except that the Holy Spirit tells me in city after city that jail and suffering lie ahead. But my life is worth nothing to me unless I use it for finishing the work assigned me by the Lord Jesus – the work of telling others the Good News about the wonderful grace of God.

"So, guard yourselves and God's people. Feed and shepherd God's flock – His church, purchased with His own blood over which the Holy Spirit has appointed you as leaders. I know that false teachers, like vicious wolves, will come in among you after I leave, not sparing the flock. Even some men from your own group will rise up and distort the truth in order to draw a following. Watch out! Remember the three years I was with you – my constant watch and care over you night and day, and my many tears for you.

"I entrust you to God and the message of His grace that is able to build you up and give you an inheritance with all those He has set apart for Himself."[3]

When I finished, I knelt and prayed with them before they escorted me down to the ship. With tears in our eyes, we embraced and kissed one another goodbye.

For the next three days, we continued to sail along the coastline of Asia to Patara in Lycia with overnight stops on the islands of Cos and Rhodes. In Patara, we boarded a Phoenician trading ship headed for Tyre. We sailed over open water for five days, passing the island of Cyprus.

When we landed at the harbor of Tyre, the captain told us the ship would remain in port for one week while he and his crew unloaded cargo and traded it for the Phoenician goods he needed for the next leg of the journey. My travel companions and I went ashore and tried to find local believers with whom we would stay.

. . .

I was surprised to see Procorus among them. It had been twelve years since he and I had parted ways in Tarsus. After exchanging greetings, I learned he had remained in Seleucia for ten years before coming here. He had actually intended to return to Jerusalem, but the Spirit had redirected him to stay in Tyre. The Tyrian church had continued to grow throughout the two years since his arrival, and their Gospel witness had spread to other cities in Syria.

We talked well past midnight as we shared with the believers how the Spirit of God was working across the provinces of Asia, Macedonia, and Achaia, and even more regions of the world including Rome.

"I remember the Day of Pentecost," Procorus remarked, "when the Holy Spirit first entered into that upper room in Jerusalem. And now, twenty-eight years later, the Gospel is spreading through the work of the Spirit to the ends of the earth. Jesus's commission is being carried out – in many ways through the precious blood of those who have been persecuted. The work is by no means finished, but look at what God has accomplished!" Spontaneously, we all began to sing hymns and give praise, rejoicing in the mighty works of God!

The next morning, Procorus and a few of the brothers shared with me their concern that I should not go to Jerusalem. They had each had visions about the danger they believed was awaiting me. I thanked them for their concern but told them, "I cannot turn back from what I know the Spirit is directing me to do. *I am willing to endure anything if it will bring salvation and eternal glory in Christ Jesus to those God has chosen.*(4)

When we returned to the ship at the end of the week, the entire congregation came to the shore to see us off. Together we knelt and prayed before saying farewell. Just before boarding the ship, I called out, "*I fully expect and hope that I will never be ashamed, but that I will continue to be bold for Christ, as I have been in the past. And I trust that my life will bring honor to Christ, whether I live or die.*(5) And I pray you will have that boldness as well!"

. . .

After a brief stop in Ptolemais, we sailed on to Caesarea Maritima. Once there, we bid our Phoenician captain and crew farewell – but only after we had baptized them along the shore as our newest brothers in Christ!

The one person I wanted to find was Philip the evangelist. He was the one remaining leader from the church in Jerusalem whom I had attempted to persecute years earlier but had yet to meet. Twenty-two years had passed, and I had not yet expressed my regret nor asked his forgiveness. This face-to-face meeting was long overdue!

When we finally arrived at his home, Philip welcomed us with open arms. When I attempted to express my regret, he immediately interrupted saying, "Brother Paul, you are not the same man who pursued us all those years ago. You are a new creation transformed by the power of the Gospel. That man no longer lives, but Christ lives in you. Whatever forgiveness was required was given by Jesus. Those sins are covered with His shed blood and have long been forgiven and forgotten. We have heard many testimonies of how God is working through you to carry the Gospel to the Gentiles. I welcome you into my home as my brother in Christ, a fellow laborer, and as my special guest. Come, join me at my table, and rest from your travels."

Over the next several days we shared with each other the great and mighty things we had seen God do. He told me about the movement of the Gospel in Samaria, about an Ethiopian official who had believed and carried the Gospel message to his homeland, and how the Gospel had spread throughout the cities of Judea along the coastline of the Mediterranean Sea. Philip was now the pastor of the growing church in Caesarea Maritima with four unmarried daughters at home, all of whom had received the gift of prophecy from the Holy Spirit. During my visit, his daughters each warned me of the danger the Lord had shown them awaiting me in Jerusalem.

. . .

While we were still there, another visitor arrived to see Philip. It was Agabus, whom I had last seen ten years earlier when he came to Antioch to warn us of a famine that would strike the entire Roman world. We all had witnessed that prophecy from the Lord come to pass. He was just returning from a pilgrimage to Jerusalem. Soon after he arrived, Agabus took my belt and bound his own hands and feet saying, *"The Holy Spirit declares, 'So shall the owner of this belt be bound by the Jewish leaders in Jerusalem and turned over to the Gentiles.'"*(6)

My traveling companions, together with Philip and the local believers, begged me not to go to Jerusalem. But I knew I must.

God had given me a clear word with a clear confirmation by His Spirit – yet, I knew I had a choice. I could choose to be disobedient to God and go the "safe" way, or I could choose to continue to walk by faith according to His Word empowered by His Spirit. I also knew God is trustworthy to keep that which I have committed to Him, including my own life, until the day of Christ's return.

Soon afterward we departed for Jerusalem. Several believers from Caesarea joined us on the journey. When we arrived in the city, we went directly to the home of my dear friend Mnason. It had been five years since I had seen him. He told me his family sent word that the work God began through Barnabas and me in Cyprus years ago was continuing to thrive and bear fruit. As a matter of fact, Barnabas and John Mark had stayed with his family when they returned to the island a few years earlier.

The next day, he took us to meet with James and the other elders of the church, and I gave them a detailed account of what God had accomplished among the Gentiles. When I finished, they praised God and reiterated their expectations of the Gentile believers as they had previously set forth in their letter: *"They should abstain from eating food offered to idols, from consuming blood or the meat of strangled animals, and from sexual immorality."*(7)

. . .

Then they turned the conversation to address the concerns Jewish Christians in Jerusalem were expressing about me. James spoke on their behalf saying, *"You know, dear brother, many thousands of Jews have also believed, and they all follow the law of Moses very seriously. But the Jewish believers here in Jerusalem have been told that you are teaching all the Jews who live among the Gentiles to turn their backs on the laws of Moses. They've heard that you teach them not to circumcise their children or follow other Jewish customs. They will certainly hear that you have come.*

"Here's what we want you to do. We have four men here who have each made a Nazirite vow. Go with them to the Temple and join them in the purification ceremony, even paying for them to have their heads ritually shaved. Then everyone will know that the rumors are all false and that you yourself observe the Jewish laws."(8)

The next day, I did as they asked and went to the temple with the four men. Since they had already started their purification ritual, I publicly announced their vows would end in seven days, and we would return on that day to offer sacrifices for each of them.

The seven days were almost up when several Jews from Ephesus saw me in the temple, falsely accused me, and began to stir up a group of Jews against me. Soon they grabbed me, yelling, *"Men of Israel, help us! This is the man who preaches against our people everywhere and tells everybody to disobey the Jewish laws. He speaks against the temple – and even defiles this holy place by bringing in Gentiles."*(9)

Apparently, the Jews had seen me walking through the streets of the city with Trophimus throughout the week and wrongly assumed I had brought him into the inner areas of the temple where Gentiles are not permitted.

Their accusations quickly spread throughout the city. A riotous mob formed demanding my death. They apprehended me and dragged me out of the temple. We hadn't gone far before I realized where they were taking me – just outside the city gates to the exact place we had stoned Stephen.

Word apparently reached the commander of the Antonio fortress that all Jerusalem was in an uproar. He immediately called out his soldiers and directed them to join him in stopping the mob. I was already being beaten when the soldiers arrived. When my captors saw the commander and his men, they immediately stopped.

The commander, whose name was Claudius, demanded to know who I was and what I had done. Some shouted one thing and some another. Since he couldn't find out the truth in all the confusion, he ordered I be bound with two chains and taken to the fortress. As the soldiers took me away, the mob followed closely behind. When we reached the stairs leading into the fortress, the mob grew so violent the soldiers had to lift me to their shoulders to protect me. The crowd pressed in even further and began to shout, *"Kill him, kill him!"*[10]

As the soldiers were about to take me inside, we passed by Claudius and I shouted at him in Greek, *"May I have a word with you?"*[11]

"Do you know Greek?" he replied with surprise. *"Aren't you the Egyptian who led a rebellion some time ago and led four thousand assassins out into the wilderness?"*[12]

"No," I replied, *"I am a Jew and a respected citizen of Tarsus in Cilicia. Please, let me talk to these people."*[13]

After a moment, the commander agreed. He directed the soldiers to face me toward the crowd while they retained their grip on me. I stood on the stairs and motioned to the people to be quiet. I spoke to them in their own language of Hebrew.

. . .

I started by sharing the story of my conversion. They listened intently as I told them that Jesus was the Messiah. But when I told them the Lord had directed me to tell the Gentiles this Good News, they erupted again. No devout Jew would have anything to do with the Gentiles! Had I not uttered that one word, I might have been released. But I had to be faithful to that which Jesus had called me – no matter the cost. I knew it was better to be a faithful prisoner than a free man who had failed to speak the truth.

Since Claudius did not understand Hebrew, he didn't know what I had said or why the crowd was rioting again. He ordered me taken inside and whipped so I might confess my crimes. Claudius did not realize his soldiers were about to commit a crime – one for which he could be discharged from his position. It was no small act to violate the rights of a Roman citizen. The penalty for the soldiers would have been a beating, and they too could possibly be discharged from service. But his punishment would be the more severe.

As I expected, Claudius acknowledged his error when he learned I was Roman citizen. He arranged to have me brought back to the temple to stand before my accusers – the Jewish high council. The commander made sure to bring an additional contingent of soldiers to keep the crowd in check. He wanted to personally hear exactly what the trouble was all about so he could officially charge me under my rights as a Roman citizen. Also, Claudius needed to have official charges in order to justify the action he had already taken against me.

As I stood before the high council, I said, *"Brothers, I am a Pharisee, as were my ancestors! And I am on trial because my hope is in the resurrection of the dead!"*[14]

Immediately the council divided, as I expected they would, and they began to argue with one another. Seeing the confusion unfold, Claudius realized no one was expressing any crime for which I should be charged. But as the argument became more heated, he was afraid they would tear me apart. For my protection, he ordered his soldiers to take me back to the fortress.

Later that night the Lord appeared to me in my jail cell and said, *"Be encouraged, Paul. Just as you have been a witness to me here in Jerusalem, you must preach the Good News in Rome as well."*[15]

God had just given me an irrefutable word. I would preach the Good News in Rome! I may currently be sitting in a jail cell in Jerusalem, but the Lord God was going to move heaven and earth to accomplish His purpose through me. From that moment on, I felt invincible. There wasn't a power on earth – or outside of this earth – that could keep me from carrying out God's appointed purpose.

The next day, Claudius permitted Hezron to visit me since he was my nephew. Hezron told me that James and the others had learned that a group of Jews had taken an oath not to eat or drink until they killed me. They had directed the leading priests and the high council to demand Claudius bring me before them again. The council was to pretend they wanted to examine my case more fully. The plan was to kill me as the soldiers were taking me to the temple.

I instructed Hezron to tell the commander what he had just told me. "Then," I said, "I want you to take Trophimus and leave Jerusalem this very hour. Mnason will assist you in making arrangements. You return to Tarsus and direct Trophimus to return to Ephesus. The religious leaders may go after the two of you if they can't get to me. You must return to your family, and join your father and Arsakes in teaching the church what you have learned during our time together, and Trophimus must do the same. May God's grace be with you both!"

I called out to one of the officers and said, *"Take this young man to the commander. He has something important to tell him."*[16] Upon hearing

Hezron's report, the commander told him, *"Don't let a soul know you told me this."*[17]

Claudius ordered two of his officers to take me that very night, under an armed guard of almost five hundred soldiers, to Caesarea. He sent a letter with me addressed to the Governor of the Iudaean province – Marcus Antonius Felix – which said, *"This man was seized by some Jews, and they were about to kill him when I arrived with the troops. When I learned that he was a Roman citizen, I removed him to safety. Then I took him to their high council to try to learn the basis of the accusations against him. I soon discovered the charge was something regarding their religious law – certainly nothing worthy of imprisonment or death. But when I was informed of a plot to kill him, I immediately sent him on to you. I have told his accusers to bring their charges before you."*[18]

Little did I realize all the twists and turns that were ahead in my journey. But then again, that had always been the case. I would rely on the Spirit to lead me according to His path!

* * *

27

That night, as ordered, the soldiers took Paul as far as Antipatris. They returned to the fortress the next morning, while the mounted troops took him on to Caesarea. When they arrived in Caesarea, they presented Paul and the letter to Governor Felix.[1]

* * *

"I *will hear your case myself when your accusers arrive,*"[2] the governor told me after reading the letter from Claudius. He directed his guards to place me in a prison cell located under his audience hall. This prison was used to hold criminals who were either soon to be crucified or awaiting transport to Rome for one reason or another.

Marcus Antonius Felix had been the Roman governor of Iudaea for approximately six years. He was known to have the disposition of a slave and the power of a tyrant. He had been appointed governor by Emperor Claudius.

Affairs between the Jewish people and the Roman rulers had further deteriorated under his governorship. His cruelty and immoral behavior were repulsive to the Jews. His fondness for receiving bribes had increased corruption and crime throughout the province. At this point, his rule had been marked by internal feuds and disturbances, which he was known to resolve with brutal severity.

In fairness, Felix had little experience ruling prior to this position. He had a very unusual path to power. He was born a slave, became a freedman, then was quickly elevated to a high government office. Felix's half brother Pallas was one of Emperor Claudius's most trusted ministers and was the one who was instrumental in Felix's appointment.

Soon after becoming governor, Felix had fallen in love with Drusilla, the beautiful daughter of King Agrippa I. When they first met, she was already the wife of Azizus, king of Emesa. She and Felix plotted for her to divorce Azizus so the two of them could marry. The whole affair reminded the Jews of Herod Antipas's adulterous relationship with Herodias and further debased Felix in their eyes.

In general, those who lived under his rule mistrusted him. A Sadducee named Jonathan had been of some assistance to Felix in securing his appointment as governor. As a result, Felix made Jonathan one of his counselors and confidants in the early days of his rule. For a time he had a positive influence on Felix's relations with the Jews. When the high priest Ananias was sent to Rome by Quadratus to answer the charges being made against him, Felix rewarded Jonathan's loyalty by naming him to the position of high priest.

In that new role, Jonathan was in an even stronger position to counsel Felix to moderate his actions so he could enjoy peaceful relations with the people and the favor of Rome. Jonathan truly wanted Felix to succeed and feared the governor's more excessive actions would cause the Jewish leaders to complain to Caesar. But Felix started resenting Jonathan's criticism and arranged to have him killed. Though Felix thought he had kept his role in Jonathan's death a secret, the Jews soon learned he was behind it. They threatened to advise the emperor of his actions, and Felix feared how Nero would react.

Ananias, having been acquitted of the charges against him, had just returned to Jerusalem. He fully expected to resume his role as high priest, particularly now that the position had suddenly been vacated. Felix realized that Ananias could easily be the solution to his problem.

Ananias was a typical Sadducee – wealthy, haughty, unscrupulous, fulfilling his office for selfish and political ends, anti-nationalist in his relation to the Jews, but conciliatory toward the Romans. He wielded great influence over the people. Ananias and Felix realized an alliance between them could work to both of their advantages. Ananias would silence the threats being made against Felix, who, in turn, would name Ananias to the position of high priest.

Five days after I was brought to the governor, Ananias arrived with some other members of the high council, confident that Felix would rule in his favor. He was joined by Tertullus, the lawyer who would prosecute me. Tertullus had gained his own reputation in the province over the years, having argued in Roman court many times before. He was a Hellenistic Jew, and the Jews had employed him to state their case before Felix. The high council had not needed a lawyer to try me in their own court, but after Claudius secretly moved me to Caesarea, they had no choice. They required an expert in Roman law to present their case appropriately.

After dispensing with the customary – and completely baseless – flattery, Tertullus charged me with creating disturbances among Romans throughout the empire to stir up revolt – an offense against the Roman government, punishable by death. Second, he charged that I was the ringleader of a rebellious sect known as the Nazarenes. I thought it was interesting he did not refer to us as Christians. That term was already being used throughout many of the provinces, but for Tertullus to do so would imply the Jews acknowledged Jesus as the "Christ" (the Messiah). Third, he charged that I had attempted to profane the temple by bringing a Gentile into it, a crime the Jews themselves were permitted to punish.

Additionally, Tertullus insinuated that Claudius and the Romans had unnecessarily escalated the matter. To hear him tell it, if Claudius had handled the situation properly, Felix would never have been involved in the first place. He insisted the charges against me had implications for the entire empire. When he was done, Ananias and the other men declared that everything Tertullus said was true.

This was undeniably a formidable attack against me. On one side was an unscrupulous religious leader and a crafty attorney presenting false charges before a crooked judge who was in many ways indebted to the religious leader. On the other side was a short, nearly blind preacher with no one to stand with me – except the only One who matters ... the Almighty God!

The Spirit reminded me that morning that I was His ambassador on His mission, journeying according to His plan. The outcome of this trial had been settled long ago. God had already declared His verdict when He told me to go preach the Gospel in Rome. These false charges were not going to change that. No fancy speech by Tertullus was going to make any difference. Ananias and Felix would be powerless to change the outcome.

Basically, I was being accused of treason against Rome. But Tertullus had presented no witnesses and no evidence to support such a charge. Felix knew there was no basis for these charges and legally should have let me go free immediately. He didn't even need to hear my defense. The prosecution had failed to make its case!

However, the governor motioned for me to rise and present my defense. Standing to my feet, I said, *"I know, sir, that you have been a judge of Jewish affairs for many years, so I gladly present my defense before you. You can quickly discover that I arrived in Jerusalem no more than twelve days ago to worship at the temple. My accusers never found me arguing with anyone in the temple, nor stirring up a riot in any synagogue or on the streets of the city. These men cannot prove the things they accuse me of doing.*

"But I admit that I follow the Way, which they call a cult. I worship the God of our ancestors, and I firmly believe the Jewish law, and everything written in the prophets. I have the same hope in God that these men have, that He will raise both the righteous and the unrighteous. Because of this, I always try to maintain a clear conscience before God and all people.

"After several years away, I returned to Jerusalem with money to aid my people and to offer sacrifices to God. My accusers saw me in the temple as I was completing a purification ceremony. There was no crowd around me and no rioting. But some Jews from the province of Asia were there – and they ought to be here to bring charges if they have anything against me! Ask these men here what crime the Jewish high council found me guilty of, except for the one time I shouted out, 'I am on trial before you today because I believe in the resurrection of the dead!'"(3)

At that moment, Felix unexpectedly adjourned the hearing saying he wanted to hear from Claudius before he made a decision. He dismissed Ananias, Tertullus, and the others, and sent me back to my prison cell. Every person in that hall made no effort to hide their surprise. Ananias thought the outcome had been guaranteed.

But God had other plans! The governor had obviously learned how to be a politician; he did not want to antagonize Ananias or the other religious leaders. And he needed the religious leaders to see him as an ally – at least in this matter. He was more concerned about doing what was politically beneficial than he was about doing what was right. He was quite content to keep me in prison because at that moment he decided it was useful for his purpose. But I knew that God had intervened so that His plans would be accomplished!

. . .

I honestly do not believe Felix ever contacted Claudius for more information or requested he come to Caesarea. If he had, Claudius would have come. He is a man under authority. Instead, I remained in prison for the next two years.

The good part of my imprisonment was I repeatedly was given opportunity to preach the Good News to Felix and Drusilla. But Felix would put off making any decision until "the next time." As the months passed, it became obvious Felix was waiting for me to bribe him so he could release me. He even made it easy by allowing my friends to visit and have access to me to provide for my needs. But I was not going to give him a bribe, so I remained a prisoner.

When time came for Felix to turn over rule of the province to Porcius Festus, it would have been customary for him to release me. But even then, Felix put his own political agenda above doing what was right.

It would have been easy to blame Felix for my extended imprisonment. But if I had, I would have missed what was really happening. This was God's plan, not Felix's. When the Holy Spirit told me I would preach the Good News in Rome, He meant I would also preach to Romans along the way.

Throughout my years following Jesus, I had experienced divine appointments, when the Spirit had led me to just the right person at just the right time. This, however, was an example of God's divine delays – seasons through which He accomplishes His work in ways we would have never foreseen.

Divine delays are not times to just sit back; rather, they are times to press forward in what we know God has called us to do. The temptation is to step out on our own to find a shortcut around the delay. But remember, His timing is perfect. He will delay until His perfect moment, and then He will hasten it!

. . .

Three days after Porcius Festus assumed his position as the new governor, he decided to go to Jerusalem. Though the Romans had declared Caesarea Maritima to be the capital of the province, he knew the Jews still saw Jerusalem as the seat of power. He decided to begin his rule by extending an olive branch of goodwill to the religious leaders. He would travel to Jerusalem to meet them for the first time.

Apparently, the religious leaders used the meeting as an opportunity to present their accusations against me. Festus invited them to follow him back to Caesarea where he would hear their evidence and decide my fate.

A week later, I was again brought to the audience hall for my case to be heard. I noticed right away that Tertullus was absent. Since he had been ineffective before Felix, the religious leaders had apparently decided to represent themselves before their new governor.

Once again, they made false accusations without witnesses or evidence. Festus came to the same conclusion as Felix – I wasn't guilty of any crime under Roman law. But my innocence did not diminish his dilemma.

One of Festus's assignments from Rome was to maintain peaceful control over this occupied nation. If he found in my favor, he would alienate the Jews and potentially disrupt the peace of what was already a fragile occupation. If he found me guilty, he would be sentencing an innocent man to death. At that moment, I am certain he was quietly blaming Felix for leaving him in this no-win situation.

Since no Roman law was broken, Festus's resolution was I should be returned to Jerusalem to be tried in the temple court. Though that remedy would not provide the religious leaders with the legal means to execute me, it would enable them to have me killed while I was being transported back to Jerusalem. So, Festus's solution was more than acceptable to the Jews.

But my response to Festus's solution caught him off guard. I appealed to Caesar! One of my rights as a Roman citizen is to appeal a decision to a higher authority. And the decisions of governors, such as Festus, could be appealed to Caesar himself. Decisions appealed to local authorities could often take as long as one to two years due to administrative backlogs. As you might imagine, the emperor's backlog was even greater.

Once a citizen requests an appeal to a higher authority, the process cannot be denied by a lower authority. That meant Festus could no longer require that I be taken to Jerusalem. He was powerless to do anything other than keep me under guard awaiting transport to Rome.

In many respects, my appeal to Caesar provided Festus with the best solution to his no-win dilemma. He was no longer compelled to do anything to an innocent man for fear of how the Jews would respond. And the Jews could no longer hold him responsible because he was powerless to decide!

Yet, I knew none of this was Festus's or my plan – it was God's plan. Long before there was a Caesar, and long before there was a Paul, God had orchestrated all of this. He had put all the pieces in place for His will to be done. And it wasn't simply for my protection; it was for the furtherance of God's plan – that I preach the Good News in Rome!

About this same time, King Agrippa II decided to pay a visit to welcome Festus as the new governor of Iudaea. King Agrippa II was the great-grandson of King Herod the Great. His father, King Agrippa I, had ruled the Iudaean province from 41 to 44 A.D. So, this Agrippa had been a teenage boy in this palace in Caesarea when his father ruled. He was now the client ruler over several cities in Galilee, Perea, and four smaller territories, while Festus, as governor, was the ruler over the Iudaean province.

Though the two men had different titles, they held equal rank in the hierarchy of Roman rule.

Agrippa's sister and incestuous lover, Bernice, accompanied him on the visit. It was a timely visit considering my imprisonment. Coming from Rome, Festus was not very knowledgeable about the religious beliefs of the Jews. When Felix was governor, he had the advantage that his wife, Drusilla, was a Jew and could counsel him about Jewish beliefs. Drusilla was, in fact, the sister of Agrippa and Bernice. They were part of the fourth generation of their family to live in this region – and all were well versed in Judaism, though their individual practices varied. Those who ruled used that understanding to curry favor with the people, while most often choosing to embrace Greco-Roman culture and religion. Festus knew Agrippa and Bernice could provide him with the necessary insight into Jewish beliefs he lacked.

I knew Festus was struggling with what explanation to give Caesar for sending me to Rome. He truly wanted to understand why the Jews were trying to kill me. But he also knew he would look foolish before the emperor if he was unable to provide official charges for a trial in Rome. Thus, he seized the opportunity to ask Agrippa for his advice.

Festus arranged for me to present my case before Agrippa in the amphitheater. In honor of Agrippa and Bernice, it was accompanied by great pomp, including military officers and prominent men from the city. The amphitheater was filled with people – more for Agrippa's sake than mine – but it still provided a great audience of Romans to hear the Good News.

Agrippa gestured for me to speak in my defense. *"I am fortunate, King Agrippa, that you are the one hearing my defense today against all these accusations made by the Jewish leaders,"* I began. *"For I know you are an expert on all Jewish customs and controversies. Now please listen to me patiently!"*[4]

. . .

I explained how I used to be a Pharisee and persecutor of those who followed The Way until I encountered Jesus on the Damascus Road. "Jesus said to me, '*For I have appeared to you to appoint you as My servant and witness. Tell people that you have seen Me and tell them what I will show you in the future. And I will rescue you from both your own people and the Gentiles. Yes, I am sending you to the Gentiles to open their eyes, so they may turn from darkness to light and from the power of Satan to God.*'"(5)

I continued, "*And so, King Agrippa, I obeyed that vision from heaven. I teach nothing except what the prophets and Moses said would happen – that the Messiah would suffer and be the first to rise from the dead, and in this way announce God's light to Jews and Gentiles alike.*"(6)

At that point, Festus interrupted saying it all sounded like craziness to him. But I replied, "*I am not insane, Most Excellent Festus. What I am saying is the sober truth. And King Agrippa knows about these things. I speak boldly, for I am sure these events are all familiar to him, for they were not done in a corner! King Agrippa, do you believe the prophets? I know you do!*'"(7)

Agrippa said, "*You almost persuade me to become a Christian.*"(8)

I replied, "*Whether quickly or not, I pray to God that both you and everyone here in this audience might become the same as I am, except for these chains.*"(9)

Agrippa, Bernice, Festus, and all the others then stood and walked out saying, "*This man hasn't done anything to deserve death or imprisonment. He could have been set free if he hadn't appealed to Caesar.*"(10)

Sadly, they had heard … but they had not listened. I was quite possibly the only "free" man in the amphitheater that day. Mine was not the plight to be pitied. Agrippa, Bernice, Festus, and probably the others who walked out were still under the bondage of their sin.

• • •

Agrippa had "almost" been persuaded. But "almost" is what had prevented him from being set free. Though I was a prisoner in their eyes, I wasn't the prisoner –they were. I pray that one day I learn some of those assembled surrendered their lives to Christ. But I know I am not responsible for how anyone responded. I wasn't then – and I never will be. My responsibility rests with being obedient to the heavenly vision of proclaiming the Gospel.

It may have been Festus who spoke the order I be sent to Rome, but I knew the One who had really given that order!

* * *

28

When the time came, we set sail for Italy.[1]

* * *

I wasn't the only prisoner being taken to Rome by Julius, the Roman centurion. But I was the only prisoner who was a Roman citizen. The other prisoners with me were to become gladiators. Rome's lust for blood was insatiable. Romans found armed combat to the death to be entertaining, so the need for new gladiators was endless.

Men were brought to Rome from the far corners of the empire. They were men without hope, headed to their deaths in the Colosseum at the hands of other gladiators or in the jaws of wild beasts. I was free on the ship to share the Good News with these men, as well as the soldiers and sailors. If there ever was a group who needed to hear about the grace of God, it was this group.

Luke and Aristarchus joined me on this journey, and I was grateful for their company. Since Festus did not consider me a dangerous criminal, and both men were Roman citizens, he had given permission for them to travel with me. However, we were required to pay our own passage. Festus was not going to have Rome's coffers pay for what he saw as my unnecessary voyage to Rome.

The home port of the ship was Adramyttium, located on the shore of the Aegean Sea near Pergamum. I had never visited this city, and to the best of my knowledge the Gospel had not yet made its way there. We were scheduled to make multiple stops at ports along the way. Our first stop was just a short way up the coast in Syria at the city of Sidon. Given my unique circumstances, Julius allowed me to go visit friends and gather additional financial provisions – for the cost of the voyage as well as expenses I would incur in Rome. I am not certain whether Julius's kindness was motivated by compassion or the prospect I would give him a financial reward.

The next day we set back out on the open seas for the port of Myra in Lycia. We quickly encountered severe headwinds, prompting the captain to change our course so we would sail on the north side of the island of Cyprus instead of the southern route. He told us our seven-day voyage would now take ten days, but it would be much smoother and safer than trying to battle the winds.

I was grateful for the additional time to speak with him and his crew about Jesus. When they all surrendered their hearts to the Lord on the ninth day, I knew God had provided that headwind for just that purpose! When we docked at Myra, my first order of business was to baptize the captain and his crew.

However, the centurion's first order of business was to arrange passage for us on an Alexandrian vessel bound for Rome. He was concerned the delay we had experienced, combined with the additional stops planned by the Adramyttian ship, would result in our arriving in Rome much too late. The winter season was fast approaching, and changes in the weather could cause even further delays. The course of the Alexandrian ship would be more direct across the open seas.

. . .

We departed the next day on the Alexandrian vessel but soon encountered the strong headwinds our previous captain had avoided. After several days of rough sailing, the Egyptian captain turned the ship toward the west, and we sailed along the southern coast of Crete. We continued to struggle against the winds and rough seas. Any time the centurion had hoped to gain by changing ships was looking doubtful. It was clearly too late in the season to attempt a long voyage across the open seas. The captain decided to make an unplanned stop at Fair Havens, near the city of Lasea, to give the crew a brief rest.

While in port, I expressed my concerns to Julius and the ship's captain saying, "*Sirs, I believe there is trouble ahead if we go on – shipwreck, loss of cargo, injuries, and danger to our lives.*[2] We should remain in this safe harbor and weather the winter."

But the ship's captain wanted to save face; he had guaranteed Julius he would get us to Italy before the weather turned bad. Julius had paid him a premium based on that promise, and the captain was not going to forfeit the money. So, he assured Julius the journey could still be made. "I have been sailing these seas all of my life," he said. "Whose opinion do you value more in this matter – mine or that of this Jewish tentmaker? Besides, this is a terrible harbor in which to spend the winter. My ship would be too exposed. I recommend we continue farther up the coast toward Phoenix and see if the weather improves."

Julius also knew his superiors would not be pleased if we remained in Fair Havens. He had been ordered to get his prisoners – particularly the other men – to Rome as quickly as possible. Further delay would not bode well for his career. So, the decision was made to continue the journey in hopes the weather improved.

As we left Fair Havens the next morning, the wind was blowing lightly from the south. It appeared the captain might be right, and this had been the correct decision. But by afternoon the weather changed abruptly, and a typhoon wind caught up with the ship and blew us off course. The captain tried to turn the ship into the wind but to no avail. Finally, he gave up and let the ship be pushed along by the gale winds.

We hoisted aboard the lifeboat we had been towing behind us. The captain gave the order to band the ship with ropes to strengthen the hull. The winds, which had raged for days, continued to batter the ship. The storm blotted out the sun and the stars, and we were surrounded by darkness. Soon the crew began throwing cargo overboard along with anything else that wasn't needed. Even the captain and experienced seamen had lost hope. None of us had eaten for days.

It was then I called out to all the men on the ship – seamen, prisoners, soldiers, and companions alike – and said to them, *"Men, you should have listened to me in the first place and not left Crete. You would have avoided all this damage and loss. But take courage! None of you will lose your lives, even though the ship will go down. For last night an angel of the God to whom I belong and whom I serve stood beside me, and He said, 'Don't be afraid, Paul, for you will surely stand trial before Caesar! What's more, God in His goodness has granted safety to everyone sailing with you.' So take courage! For I believe God. It will be just as He said. But we will be shipwrecked on an island."*[3]

About midnight on the fourteenth night of the storm, as we were being driven across the sea, the sailors sensed land was near. They dropped a weighted line and found the water was 36 meters deep. A little later they measured again and found it was only 27 meters deep. They were afraid we would be driven against the rocks along the shore, so they threw out four anchors from the back of the ship in an attempt to slow us down. They called out to their gods. But nothing happened – the sailors were certain our destruction and death were imminent.

Soon, the captain made the decision to abandon ship but knew we could not all fit into the lifeboat. There were 276 of us on board. The sailors lowered the lifeboat as though they were going to put out anchors from the front of the ship. Aristarchus overheard them as they were plotting and came to me. I immediately went to Julius and the soldiers saying, *"We will all die unless the sailors stay aboard."*[4] The centurion commanded the soldiers to cut the ropes to the lifeboat and let it drift away.

Just as morning began to dawn, I urged everyone to eat. *"You have been so worried that you haven't touched food for two weeks,"* I said. *"Please eat something now for your own good. For not a hair of your heads will perish."*[5] Then I took some bread, gave thanks to God before them all, and broke off a piece and ate it. Soon everyone began to eat, and I saw the hopelessness on their faces begin to fade. After we had eaten, the sailors lightened the ship even more by throwing the remaining cargo of wheat overboard.

The morning sky began to lighten, revealing a coastline ahead. No one, including the captain, recognized where we were. But soon one of the sailors called out that he could see a bay with a beach. I thought back to that day years earlier when the welcome sight of the Cyprus coastline had emerged through a storm. God had kept us safe that day – and I knew He would again. I prayed we would not be tossed about in the sea like we were on that occasion, but would all make our way safely to shore.

The captain decided to get to shore by running the ship aground. He gave the order to cut away the anchors and leave them in the sea. Then he ordered the rudders be lowered and the foresail raised as he set our heading toward shore. We hadn't traveled very far when we hit a shoal and the ship ran aground farther out than the captain anticipated. The bow of the ship stuck fast, while the stern was repeatedly being smashed by the force of the waves. Soon the ship began to break apart.

The soldiers decided to kill the prisoners to ensure we didn't swim ashore and escape. As they raised their weapons, I called out to the centurion, "Remember, none of us will be lost if we stay together!"

Julius ordered his soldiers to stand down and then told those who could swim to jump overboard and head to land. Those who could not swim were told to hold on to planks or debris from the broken ship. After an hour, we all made it to shore safely, despite the torrential rain. Each one of us lay there on land thanking God for saving us. The people of the island ran to give us aid, greeting us with open arms of compassion.

It was mid-November, the wind was biting cold, and we were soaked. The first order of business was to build a fire. Everyone from the ship, along with the islanders, pitched in to search for dry wood. As I added my armful of sticks to the pile, a poisonous snake crawled out, bit me, and affixed itself to my hand. The residents, believing me to be a criminal, thought justice was seeking its revenge. Several exclaimed, "*A murderer, no doubt! Though he escaped the sea, justice will not permit him to live.*"[6]

They expected me to fall dead as punishment for my crimes. Even though these pagan people had never heard about God's redemptive love, they still believed in right and wrong. They had a sense of justice and that sin deserves to be punished.

They had a sense of morality. They understood sin – and the penalty for sin. Where did that come from?

Their sense of morality and sin was God-given. They already knew the truth that *God shows His anger from heaven against all sinful, wicked people who suppress the truth by their wickedness. They know the truth about God because He has made it obvious to them.*[7]

The people stared as I shook off the snake into the fire. Most people would react with panic and flail in horror at such a snake bite. But I knew it could not harm me – and as they watched, they realized I was unaffected. The only death to occur that day was that of the snake. The islanders decided I was no ordinary man. They were wrong when they thought me to be a god, but they were right that I was no ordinary man – I am a redeemed man.

. . .

I told them the snake is a reminder that Satan is a defeated foe. And one day he will be burned up in the fire. We do not live in fear of him or in panic over his power. He is powerless over us – not because of anything we can do – but because we have been redeemed by the blood of the Lamb, and we are indwelt by His Holy Spirit.

Near where we landed was an estate belonging to Publius, the chief official of the island. He welcomed us and treated us kindly. On the second day, having witnessed the miracle regarding the snake, Publius told me his father was ill with fever and dysentery. The Spirit prompted me to go and pray for him. I laid my hands on him, and God healed him. Soon, all the sick people on the island came and were also healed. They showered us with honors.

Over the next three months, the residents of the island – as well as the survivors of the shipwreck – all heard and witnessed the power of the Gospel as Luke, Aristarchus, and I preached and lived it out. Through the miracles they saw and the words they heard, many came to faith and were baptized along the shoreline that had been the site of our rescue.

After winter passed, we set sail on another ship that had safely wintered in the harbor of the island. It was another Alexandrian ship with the carved image of twin Roman gods as its figurehead. The residents of the village graciously supplied us with everything we needed for the remainder of our journey. Our first stop was Syracuse on the coast of Sicily, where we stayed for three days. From there we sailed across to Italy, arriving at the town of Rhegium. A day later a south wind began blowing so we sailed around the peninsula and up the coast to the port of Puteoli, which is 200 kilometers southeast of Rome. It was this ship's final destination, so we disembarked and made the remainder of our journey over land by foot.

We remained in Puteoli for a week and regained our "land legs" before setting out along the Appian Way to Rome. About seventy kilometers outside of Rome, we encountered a group of believers who had come searching for me. Apparently, word had reached the believers in Rome of my expected arrival.

They joined us as we traveled another fifteen kilometers to the village of The Three Taverns, where we encountered a second group of men and women who were also seeking me. The journey from Jerusalem to Rome had taken slightly less than three years, including my two-year imprisonment in Caesarea. After all the difficulties we had experienced along the way, the welcome reception by these believers was a great encouragement to my spirit.

The journey had followed many unexpected twists and turns. We had met many Gentiles along the way, many of whom were now brothers and sisters in Christ. The journey had never been just about the destination – but then again, none of our journeys ever are. We praised God with these Roman believers as we told them everything God had done during those months.

But one man gave me particular cause for rejoicing as I looked across the table at him. He returned my gaze and gave me a small nod. When we began this journey, I had been his captive … and he, my captor. He hadn't really known then he was captive to his sin. But now he had been set free. Julius, the centurion, was now my brother in Christ!

* * *

29

When we arrived in Rome, Paul was permitted to have his own private lodging, though he was guarded by a soldier.[1]

* * *

Once we arrived in Rome, Julius and his soldiers took the prisoners to the headquarters of the Praetorian prefect, Sextus Afranius Burrus, to receive further orders. Those who were to become gladiators were to be taken to the Circus Maximus for training. A number of those men had become followers of Jesus during our journey, though many still rejected Him. I prayed over those who would permit me to do so before they were taken away.

Julius requested an audience with Prefect Burrus to determine what should be done with me. He had confided in me a few days earlier that he was willing to help me escape. I reminded him I was coming to Rome under the direction of the Spirit of God. I had no desire to escape from His control or His mission. I was in His hands, as I had been ever since that day on the road outside of Damascus. My fate did not rest in the hands of Emperor Nero; it rested solely in the hands of God.

. . .

I thanked him for his concern because I knew he had not made the offer lightly. I realized that if any of his prisoners escaped, including me, he would be held accountable – and that punishment could easily include death. Julius was offering to die so I could go free, but I reminded him that I was already free!

Julius presented the prefect with the letter about me from Governor Festus. Prefect Burrus checked with his aides and learned that no one had appeared in Rome to bring evidence against me. I would not be permitted to appeal to the emperor without any charges to appeal. The prefect questioned the wisdom of Festus in having me brought to Rome and mine in making an appeal. Nonetheless, I was a prisoner to be held until my accusers arrived. The prefect would arrange to have my name added to the list of people awaiting their appeal before the emperor. Based on his current backlog, it would easily be two years before that happened.

Since space was at a premium in prison and Rome was not going to pay for my long-term care, I had to find my own housing and pay my own expenses. I was still a prisoner, though, so I would be chained to a guard twenty-four hours a day. Julius took me to the Tullianum to see the head jailer so I could be registered and a contingent of guards assigned to me. I would also be responsible to pay the four guards' wages.

Luke and Aristarchus were exploring the city to find a suitable dwelling for us. We learned that over 4 million people lived in Rome. It was at least ten times larger than any city any of us had ever visited. Though we had seen examples of Roman architecture in other cities across the empire, nothing compared with the grandness of the city itself. But most everything we saw pointed to the worship of false gods or a depraved worship of self. For all its architectural majesty, the very foundation of the city was idolatrous pagan worship. There was no question God brought us to this city to preach His Good News.

Luke and Aristarchus quickly located a place for us to lodge. They were modest rooms in the heart of the city on an upper floor with good natural light and ventilation. I was extremely grateful the people in Sidon and Malta had provided me with resources for my initial expenses. I would send out word to the other churches to let them know of my financial needs so they could partner in the advance of the Gospel in Rome.

Three days after our arrival, I sent a message to the local Jewish leaders and invited them to come speak with me. I explained that my circumstances prevented me from coming to them. When they arrived, I said to them, *"Brothers, I was arrested in Jerusalem and handed over to the Roman government, even though I had done nothing against our people or the customs of our ancestors. The Romans tried me and wanted to release me, because they found no cause for the death sentence. But when the Jewish leaders protested the decision, I felt it necessary to appeal to Caesar, even though I had no desire to press charges against my own people. I asked you to come here today so we could get acquainted and so I could explain to you that I am bound with this chain because I believe that the hope of Israel – the Messiah – has already come."*(2)

They replied, *"We have had no letters from Judea or reports against you from anyone who has come here. But we want to hear what you believe, for the only thing we know about this movement is that it is denounced everywhere."*(3)

A large number of people gathered at my lodgings. I explained and testified about the kingdom of God and tried to persuade them about Jesus from the Scriptures. Using the law of Moses and the books of the prophets, I spoke to them from morning until evening. Some were persuaded by the things I said, but others did not believe. One young man who believed in Jesus that day was Justus. He was a constant companion throughout the remainder of my time in Rome, even though most of his Jewish friends abandoned him.

Many of the Jews continued to deny everything I said to the point I could no longer be heard over their loud arguments. When the din finally died down, I gave them this final word:

"The Holy Spirit was right when He said to your ancestors through Isaiah the prophet, 'Go and say to this people: When you hear what I say, you will not

understand. When you see what I do, you will not comprehend. For the hearts of these people are hardened, and their ears cannot hear, and they have closed their eyes – so their eyes cannot see, and their ears cannot hear, and their hearts cannot understand, and they cannot turn to Me and let Me heal them.' So I want you to know that this salvation from God has also been offered to the Gentiles, and they will accept it."[(4)]

After that my dwelling never lacked people seeking to hear about the kingdom of God. The Spirit had truly opened a door for me to preach the Gospel without retribution. I was already a prisoner chained to a Roman guard – no one was going to attempt to take action against me! Even the guards had no choice but to listen as I preached, taught, and prayed. And I delighted in watching as the Spirit came over the guards and they, too, became brothers in Christ.

Julius did not return to Caesarea Maritima. After giving his report of the events surrounding our travels to Rome, Prefect Burrus promoted him. He became part of the Praetorian guard, an elite unit within the Roman army, stationed in Rome. A regular visitor to my living quarters, Julius often brought fellow soldiers to hear the teachings of the Good News. Over time, a number of soldiers within the Praetorian guard also became followers of Jesus.

During one of the soldiers' visits, as they gathered around me all dressed in their armor, I said, "None of you would ever consider disobeying your commander's order nor would you allow yourself to be *tied up in the affairs of civilian life, for then you would not be pleasing the officer who enlisted you.*[(5)] In the same manner, walk faithfully in your calling as a good soldier of Christ Jesus.

"Not one of you would ever go into battle without wearing every part of your armor. You would be a disgrace to those who have sent you out and ill-prepared for your duty. The same is true as you follow our Lord Jesus Christ. Be faithful each day to *put on every piece of God's armor so you will be able to resist the enemy in the time of evil. Then after the battle you will still be standing firm. Stand your ground, putting on the belt of truth and the body armor of God's righteousness. For shoes, put on the peace that comes from the Good News so that you will be fully prepared. In addition to all of these, hold up the shield of faith to stop the fiery arrows of the devil. Put on salvation as your helmet, and take the sword of the Spirit, which is the word of God. Stay alert and be persistent in your prayers."*(6)

One day, Julius brought one of his commanding officers and the officer's mother to meet me. He was about ten years younger than I was and had the distinguished appearance of a man in authority. He and his mother's noble gait affirmed they were part of Roman society, but they both also demonstrated an air of humility. The officer's name was Pontius Aquila and his mother's name was Claudia. After Julius introduced us, Pontius Aquila began to tell me his story.

"I was named after my great-grandfather," he began. "He served as a member of the tribunal under Julius Caesar until the emperor confiscated some of our family's land in Naples to lavish it upon his mistress as a gift. From that day forward, my great-grandfather became one of the leaders of the opposition, which ultimately led to the emperor's downfall and the birth of our republic.

"My grandfather, Pontius Cominus, served with distinction as an officer of the legionary cavalry and later as a member of the Senate. My father also served Rome with distinction. More than likely, you are familiar with him – his name was Pontius Pilate. He served as the fifth prefect of the Iudaean province for ten years before being brought back to Rome to serve in the Senate until he died ten years ago.

"I spent my years as a youth in the palace in Caesarea Maritima. My mother and I were both in Jerusalem when the religious leaders brought Jesus of Nazareth before my father. I watched from the roof as my father condemned Jesus to die on the cross. My father knew He was innocent, and so did my mother and I.

. . .

"Tears flowed down our cheeks as we watched my father refuse to stand up for what was right before that crowd. I watched in shame as he ceremoniously washed his hands. It was a turning point in my life. Until that moment, I would have followed my father anywhere.

"When the soldiers led Jesus to the cross, I covered myself with a cloak and followed from a distance. I watched as He was crucified under my father's order. I knew He was not only an innocent Man, falsely accused – I knew He was a righteous man and so did my mother. I later heard He had risen from the grave, though my father denied the reports. He contended that Jesus's disciples had moved His body. But I never believed that.

"Julius tells me you are a disciple of Jesus – that He speaks to you and has even given you miraculous powers of healing. My mother and I have come because we want to hear more about Him."

For the next several hours, I told them about Jesus and His saving grace. Before the sun had set, they had become followers of Jesus. Aristarchus took them to a nearby bath and baptized them. Mother and son became active leaders in the growing church in Rome. Claudia became one of the local believers who regularly ministered to me and made sure my needs were being met. They both became faithful witnesses of the Good News.

As a matter of fact, Aquila led a man named Pudens and his wife, Priscilla, to faith in Christ. Pudens's father was a member of the Senate, and Pudens was expected to follow in his father's footsteps. Another man, Linus, also came to believe in Jesus through the witness of Aquila. Both Pudens and Linus became leaders in the church and were often by my side. All three families generously provided for my needs while I was in Rome.

Another dear brother who came to believe soon after I arrived was Eubulus. His family owned the rooms where I was staying, and he himself lived in the rooms beside mine. He not only became a great help to me throughout my time in Rome, but he also opened his home to host my many companions who came to encourage me.

One of my first traveling companions to arrive was John Mark. Although I was surprised to see him at my door, I was grateful for the time to finally settle the differences between us. Mark said after he and Barnabas traveled across Cyprus, Simon Peter had invited him to go to Rome. Together they had preached the Gospel and seen many come to faith. With Mark's help, I was able to connect the new believers I'd seen come to faith with the local church that had already been established.

I realized that my role in Rome was not to begin the work – the Spirit had already used Peter and Mark to do that. My role was to continue in the work. We both acknowledged how God had ordered John Mark's steps that day in Perga. He had set our feet on a different path – but all for the same kingdom purpose. I sought John Mark's forgiveness for the ill-will I had held toward him, and we began our relationship anew.

After Peter left Rome to go to Corinth, John Mark said he had remained for two reasons. First, he wanted to nurture the new believers and leaders; second, he had needed to fulfill a task given to him by Simon Peter. John Mark had written a complete account of the ministry, crucifixion, and resurrection of Jesus based on his interviews with Simon Peter. He also had spoken with others in the Jerusalem church, but it was primarily Simon Peter's recollections. It was the first written account about Jesus of which I was aware!

I, along with the others in the room, listened intently as he read the chronicle to us. That was the day I learned John Mark had been in the garden the night Jesus was arrested. He was only a teenager, and he had secretly followed Jesus and the disciples from the upper room to the garden that night. After Jesus was arrested, the mob discovered John Mark hiding in the bushes and tried to grab him. Mark said he broke free from their grip, but they had held onto his cloak as he ran off naked into the night. He told us he had never shared that story with anyone because he was ashamed that he had abandoned Jesus. I reminded him that he was not the only one who had abandoned Jesus!

Luke and John Mark struck up a friendship that day. Luke, of course, had become one of my most trusted travel companions with a desire to record the events surrounding the birth of the church. Mark was in a similar position with Simon Peter. The two of them would have great insights into the events going back to the incarnation of Jesus. It became clear they would become collaborators in capturing these truths and events for all who would follow.

It wasn't long before Timothy arrived bringing news of the churches in Ephesus and Philippi. I was thrilled to be reunited with him. Everyone had lifted my spirits but none so much as Timothy. I praised the Lord for his safe arrival. Epaphroditus, another dear brother from Philippi, had accompanied him on the journey.

A few weeks later, they were followed by Tychicus who brought word on the churches in Colossae and Laodicea. Demas and Onesimus came with him. Demas had been one of my companions on my last journey through Macedonia and Greece. Onesimus was another brother in Christ whom I had led to faith. He had been an indentured bondservant to another brother, Philemon, who was one of the elders of the church of Colossae. Apparently, Onesimus had now run away from his master to make this journey to Rome.

After hearing the reports from the churches, I set about sending them letters with the assistance of Timothy and Aristarchus. These men painstakingly helped me commit the words of correction, affirmation, and encouragement I believed the Lord wanted me to share with them. To the Ephesians, I wrote to remind them they are the body of Christ. I wrote, *"I pray that Christ will be more and more at home in your hearts as you trust in Him. May your roots go down deep into the soil of God's marvelous love."*[7]

. . .

The church in Philippi is probably closer to my heart than any other. Their love for me and mine for them has been deeply rooted from the start. I wanted to thank them for their constant help throughout my times of need, but I also wanted to encourage them to remain true to the Lord. I told them, "*Fix your thoughts on what is true and honorable and right. Think about things that are pure and lovely and admirable. Think about things that are excellent and worthy of praise. Keep putting into practice all you learned from me and heard from me and saw me doing, and the God of peace will be with you.*"(8)

To the churches in Colossae and Laodicea, I wrote to remind them of the supremacy of Christ in the church and how they must submit to Him in all things. "*Since God chose you to be the holy people whom He loves, you must clothe yourselves with tenderhearted mercy, kindness, humility, gentleness, and patience. You must make allowance for each other's faults and forgive the person who offends you. Remember the Lord forgave you, so you must forgive others!*"(9)

Finally, I wrote a personal letter to Philemon that he might receive Onesimus back with the same gentleness he would extend to me. Onesimus had been wrong to run away, and he knew he must return. But Philemon needed to receive him back as a brother in Christ. I wrote, "*I am boldly asking a favor of you. I could demand it in the name of Christ because it is the right thing for you to do, but because of our love, I prefer just to ask you. Take this as a request from your friend Paul, an old man, now in prison for the sake of Christ Jesus. Show kindness to Onesimus. I am sending him back to you, and with him comes my own heart.*"(10)

I bade farewell to many of my brothers as they returned to their homes with my letters in hand. Only Luke, Aristarchus, Timothy, and John Mark remained with me, as did my Roman brothers and sisters.

I had now been under house arrest for two years. My accusers from Jerusalem had never made an appearance. I could not be granted an appointment to appeal before the emperor if there was no one to make a charge. So, Pontius Aquila, Pudens, and Julius appealed to Prefect Burrus for my release, and it was granted. I hadn't been given the opportunity to proclaim the Good News to the emperor, but the Spirit had given me the opportunity to preach to many others – some of whom may preach it to the emperor themselves one day.

Luke and Aristarchus set off with me as I departed for Macedonia. John Mark embarked for Antioch to join Simon Peter, and Timothy set out for Ephesus. The Spirit gave me a peace our work in Rome was done … at least for now.

30

Timothy, as I urged you when I was going to Macedonia, remain at Ephesus.(1)

* * *

After being under house arrest for two years, I thanked God for the freedom of being released from my chains and being able to enjoy the outdoors once more. Our journey from Rome to Appii Forum took two days. I soaked in the sunshine and the vivid colors of spring as we traveled south along the Appian Way. Justus and Eubulus accompanied Luke, Aristarchus, and me as far as the port. After they helped us find a coastal trading boat that would get us to Sicily, they returned to Rome.

The seas were calm, and the winds were light as we traveled along the coastline of Italy. After five days, we arrived at Messina on the northeast point of Sicily. The first thing we did was secure our passage on a ship headed to Nicopolis. It was a Macedonian trade ship and the captain told us they would depart in five days. We set out to make the most of the days the Lord had given us in this city.

. . .

There was no synagogue, so we made our way to the center square where I began to preach the Good News. The people could tell I was a Jew, and my companions were Gentiles. They were surprised we were traveling together and that we worshiped the same God. As we told them more about Jesus, they were shocked that the Son of God would come to earth to sacrifice His own life for us and pay the price for our sins. They had never heard of a god like that! The crowd of interested listeners began to grow.

A man who I could tell was respected by the crowd came to hear us one afternoon. They parted to make a way so he could approach us. His name was Aristocles, a teacher and philosopher in the city; he also was a worshiper of the god Serapis. He told us he was familiar with the Hebrew God and saw great similarity with the god he worshiped. "Serapis," he said, "is also a supreme god. He has been revered over the centuries by both the Egyptians and the Greeks. He forms a bridge between all of our gods and reigns over them."

Aristocles had not come to debate us but to learn. I took him back to the very beginning and told him the story of creation and how sin had entered the hearts of Adam and Eve. He had heard parts of the story and nodded in agreement as I talked about the consequence of sin.

Then I told him, and all who were gathered around us, about God's promise of a Savior and how that promise was fulfilled in Jesus. I told them how the religious leaders of my people, the Jews, had rejected Jesus and put Him to death on a cross. "But Jesus did not remain in the tomb," I said. "He conquered death and the grave and rose again! I was not always a follower of Jesus. As a devout Jew I persecuted His followers. Until one day He appeared to me personally."

It was my personal encounter with Jesus that drew Aristocles deeper into conversation. "I have believed in Serapis all of my life," he said. "I have taught about him most of my adult life. But I have never had a personal encounter with him, and neither has anyone else to the best of my knowledge. He has never sacrificed himself for us; he has always demanded that we sacrifice ourselves for him!"

Before the day was over, Aristocles became a follower of Jesus. He was the first of many to be baptized along the shore of the strait that day. For the rest of our time in the city, we taught Aristocles and the others from the Scriptures. When it was time for us to leave, I told them to remain surrendered to the Spirit of the Lord and allow Him to teach them in their newfound faith in Christ. We prayed over them as they gathered on the dock to bid us farewell, asking God to sustain them in the days ahead.

One week later we docked on the island of Crete where I was to meet up with Titus, whom I had sent on before me. We had heard that a group of Jews from Crete had been in Jerusalem on the Day of Pentecost and had responded to Simon Peter's sermon. When they returned home, they had introduced the Good News to their fellow countrymen.

But those believers had failed to nurture that passion and belief in the truths of the Scripture and the leading of the Spirit. Over time, they had become lukewarm in their faith. Cretans are known for their untruthfulness and immorality, and those passions of the flesh had quickly returned. Sadly, most of the few believers on the island had become carnal Christians.

Over the next several weeks, we traveled from city to city preaching the Good News. The Spirit of the Lord went before us preparing hearts to receive His message of salvation and many came to faith. After two months, I knew I needed to continue to Nicopolis on the western shore of the province of Epirus. I left Titus there to continue the work.

Our voyage to Nicopolis on a Macedonian trading ship took us eight days. Nicopolis means "the city of victory." It was founded by Caesar Augustus in commemoration of his victory over Antony and Cleopatra. It was intended to represent the new beginnings of the Roman empire as a republic. It was adorned with monuments financed by the spoils of war, as well as the patronage of Herod the Great. It boasted two ports and all the entrapments of a great, free city. It was more Roman than the Macedonian cities that surrounded it.

When we arrived, I discovered an enclave of Jews living in the city. Their presence dated back to the days of Herod, but they appeared to have had little influence on the city. I went to the local synagogue on the first Sabbath after my arrival, but they would have nothing to do with me or my teachings about Jesus. I never returned to the synagogue but received a release from the Spirit to proclaim the kingdom of God to the Gentiles, from whom I witnessed an overwhelming response.

One of the first Gentiles to believe was Lucius, a young philosopher and teacher in the city. He had been born in the city but had traveled to Rome to study under stoic philosopher Seneca the younger. He had only recently returned to the city with his young wife, Vetus. Lucius was filled with questions, but it was clear he was not a cynic; he was a sincere seeker of truth.

We spent several days discussing the Scripture and how Jesus had fulfilled the promises given by God. As we spoke, others would come and listen to a portion of our conversation and then be on their way. On the fifth day, Lucius brought Vetus with him. He had obviously repeated to her much of what I had told him. She demonstrated an excellent grasp of the truth. In fact, the Spirit of God used her to convict Lucius the time for doubt and debate was over. It was time for them to surrender their lives to Jesus.

Many others followed when they saw the couple's response. Vetus was great with child when I baptized her and Lucius that day in the waters of the harbor. The crowd was amazed that she would do such a thing in her condition. I knew from that moment God was going to use this couple to multiply the Gospel throughout the world. Two weeks later, Vetus gave birth to their son, whom they named Polycarp. It was a joy for me to lead them as they committed themselves to raising their son in the admonition of the Lord. I had no doubt he would one day be used by the Spirit to do great things for the cause of Christ!

After two months, I decided to delay my planned journey to Spain for another six months so I could stay in Nicopolis through the winter. I sent word to Tychicus in Colossae to go to the island of Crete and take over the work there so Titus could come join me. He would be better suited to train Lucius, Vetus, and the other believers and to continue the work after my departure.

Those six months passed quickly. As Luke, Aristarchus, and I stood on the deck of the Spanish ship that would take us to Hispania Tarraco, I prayed over the large crowd of believers that had come to say goodbye. I committed them to the Lord and entrusted them to Titus. The three-week voyage to the Spanish coast was without incident.

Soon after I arrived in Tarraco, a young man named Rufus approached me in the square while I was preaching. He told me he and his family were from Cyrene, and his father's name was Simon. He was the man pulled from the crowd by the Roman soldiers to carry the cross of Jesus. There at the foot of my Savior's cross, Simon had surrendered his life. Rufus told me his father had carried Jesus's body from Golgotha to the tomb and was one of the people in the upper room the night Jesus appeared to His disciples.

"When my father returned to Cyrene," Rufus told me, "he told my mother, my brother, and me all about Jesus. He told us Jesus was the promised Messiah and shared all he had witnessed firsthand. There was no denying the reality of the truth my father told us and the change we saw in his life. We also surrendered our lives to Jesus that day. That was thirty-five years ago.

"From then, the Lord led me to sit under the teaching of the elders of the church in Jerusalem for several years and then return to Cyrene to preach the Good News. Several months ago, the Spirit of the Lord came to me in a vision and told me I was to come to Tarraco. He told me I would meet a man whom I was to help in proclaiming the Good News among the Spanish people. Today, as I listened to you preach, the Lord has shown me you are that man. I humbly place myself before you to help you in any way I can."

I rejoiced in Rufus's testimony and thanked the Lord for His faithfulness to raise up His workers to accomplish His task. During the next eighteen months as we traveled throughout the province, I saw how God had brought all of us together for His purpose in that place. When the Lord subsequently led me to return to Corinth, I left Rufus there to continue the work with the many new believers we had seen come to faith.

Two weeks later, Luke, Aristarchus, and I arrived in Corinth. In the last letter I sent the church, I promised to return to them. I wasn't coming to rebuke them for their actions or deal with them harshly. I had already corrected them through my letters. I had come to build them up. I also did not want to tell them exactly how to put their faith into practice. Rather, I wanted to help them learn how to follow the Spirit of the Lord in a way that honors Him and brings joy to their lives.

Gratefully, the divisions had passed. Those who had been causing conflict in the church had been rightly disciplined, were truly repentant, and appropriately restored. Those who had not previously repented of impurity, sexual immorality, and pursuit of lustful pleasures now began to do so. Over the next few months, we reinforced the truths we had already taught them and strengthened the leaders in their understanding and practice.

One day, Justus arrived with a message for me from the believers in Rome. Simon Peter had been crucified on a cross! The news wounded my heart like a dagger.

. . .

"Several months ago, a fire broke out in one of the cook shops situated along the side of the Circus Maximus," Justus said. "It was a windy day, and the fire spread quickly. It took nine days before it could be contained. The fire destroyed a substantial part of the city, leaving many dead and many others homeless. The surviving citizens of Rome became incensed against Emperor Nero. Why had he not led the city to react more quickly to extinguish the fire? There were some who said he had set the fire himself.

"He quickly took action to divert the blame from himself to the Christians. He announced we were a threat to the empire. He accused us of being a troublemaking people who followed a leader who had been crucified in Jerusalem because of His acts of rebellion. He told the people their city – and the entire empire – needed to be purged of Christians before they destroyed the empire. He sent out troops to arrest them. Our Christian brothers in the senate and the military attempted to speak reason to him, but he would not listen.

"He has begun gathering up Christians and having them crucified on the streets of Rome as a spectacle for the entire city. He heard Peter was one of the leaders of the movement. He sent out soldiers to apprehend him at once. There was no trial. Nero had him crucified immediately.

"Peter told his executors he was unworthy to be crucified in the same manner as his Savior, so he asked to be hung on the cross upside down. A spirit of grief and mourning has fallen upon the believers throughout the city, and many are now hiding out of fear."

As I grieved, I thought back to a conversation Peter and I once had. "In one of my last conversations with Jesus, He told me, *'I tell you the truth, when you were young, you were able to do as you liked; you dressed yourself and went wherever you wanted to go. But when you are old, you will stretch out your hands, and others will dress you and take you where you don't want to go.'*"(2)

. . .

"Jesus was telling me," Peter continued, "that one day I, too, will be taken to a cross. I do not look ahead to that day with fear, because I know on that day I will be reunited with my Lord. Rather, I look to that day as one who is unworthy to die in the same manner as my Savior."

I thanked the Spirit for granting Peter the way to bring glory to Christ even through his death. Aristarchus assisted me in writing a letter to the believers in Rome, in which I said:

"Dear brothers and sisters, stand firm and keep a strong grip on all that we taught you – both in person and by letter. Allow our Lord Jesus Christ and God our Father, who loves you and in His special favor gives us everlasting comfort and hope, to comfort your hearts and give you strength.

"Don't be surprised by the trials you are going through, as if something strange is happening. Instead, be grateful to the Lord that He has deemed you worthy to partner with Him in His suffering. He has given you His Spirit to walk with you every step of the way so that His glory is revealed through your lives.

"The Lord has shown me that in a little while I will return to you. But until I do, stand firm and remain confident with your eyes on Jesus."

Justus returned to Rome with my letter, and soon afterward the Lord showed me it was time for me to continue my travels to Macedonia.

When we entered the streets of Philippi, the believers greeted us warmly. Soon, our brother Epaphroditus emerged from their midst and embraced me. He had ministered to me faithfully for several months in Rome and had delivered my letter to the Philippian church. While he was still with me in Rome, he had become seriously ill, and we thought he would die. But God, in His mercy, had healed him. I could see his illness was gone, and he had returned to full strength.

• • •

Two of the sisters in Philippi – Euodia and Syntyche – also approached us from the crowd. While I was in Rome, I heard that a disagreement between them was causing contention in the church. Gratefully, they had received my admonition to take their argument before the Lord. They had humbly submitted their differences to God, and He had healed their relationship and the turmoil it had created within the church.

My heart was refreshed as the Lord allowed me to remain in Philippi for the next three months. But then He showed me it was time to go. Our travels continued for another two years to the churches throughout Asia, encouraging them and proclaiming the Gospel. In many of the cities where God had given me the joy of seeing the first believer come to faith, there were now thriving churches – not perfect churches – but churches made up of believers striving to honor Christ and make His name known.

I reflected on the fact that Christ's church had begun with a handful of disciples gathered in an upper room on the Day of Pentecost, and now His Gospel had multiplied across cities, provinces, and nations throughout the world. And He had chosen to accomplish His work through imperfect people – including an unworthy tentmaker from Tarsus.

The Spirit eventually led us to return to Troas – the city where He had first called me to go to the people in Macedonia. We spent three months there. Several days after we arrived, I was surprised to encounter Alexander the metal worker. I had not seen him since that day in Ephesus eleven years earlier when he and other Jews had attempted to use the riot – started by Demetrius the silversmith against me and other believers – to his advantage. His plans had failed, however, and his reputation in the city had been destroyed. Apparently, he had left Ephesus in disgrace and come to Troas to rebuild his life.

I had no idea how much he blamed me for his disgrace, nor was I aware of how his disdain for Christians and the Gospel had continued to grow. While we were going about our business encouraging the believers in Troas and preaching the Gospel, Alexander was secretly plotting against us. He was aware of Nero's hatred for Christians and convinced the governor of the city he would earn the emperor's favor by having me arrested and taken to Rome for execution.

Alexander enlisted the assistance of several allies in fabricating testimony that I, along with other leaders of the church in the city, were supporting rebellion against Rome.

Early one morning, soldiers arrived at my door to arrest me. Alexander accompanied them to identify me and bear witness against me. I saw a smile of satisfaction on his face as the soldiers bound my hands and led me away.

The trial took place quickly with the governor presiding over it. I was not permitted to have any witnesses speak on my behalf because they were all accused of being complicit in my actions. The false charges from Alexander and his confederates were unchallenged except by me. Within hours, I was declared guilty of treason, and the governor ordered I be taken to Rome for execution. He prepared a letter to the emperor detailing the charges against me that would be carried by the guards accompanying me. He seemed certain Nero would have me executed in Rome and reward him for his swift action.

I again found myself in chains, shackled to four Roman guards. Evidently, even the timing of my arrest had been worked out in advance. A ship was already at the docks preparing to sail to Rome. I was on that ship headed out to sea the same day I was arrested. I was not permitted to have anyone travel with me, though Luke and Aristarchus arranged to follow me.

I also was not granted permission to engage in any conversation with the guards or the crew throughout my journey. So, I spent the next eighteen days in silence, which gave me the opportunity to speak with my Lord … and Him alone.

31

Remember my chains.[1]

* * *

After an uneventful voyage, we arrived at the harbor city of Ostia, on the outskirts of Rome. This time I would not be making a long journey over land to arrive in the city, and I would not be greeted along the way by fellow believers.

Rome was now very different from the city I had arrived in eight years prior. It had been over two-and-one-half years since the fire had destroyed much of the city. Though much rebuilding had already occurred, there still were many physical reminders of the devastation that had taken place.

But much more visible than the physical signs was the deathly pallor that had now befallen the city. The crosses scattered along the roads cast their shadow of death in every corner of the city. I wept as I saw my brothers and sisters hanging on the crosses – many near death. I asked the Lord to comfort them and give them strength to endure their final moments of agony before they entered His presence.

. . .

I knew our Lord was only too aware of the pain they were experiencing. I found myself asking Jesus if He could return at that very moment so these men and women would not need to endure any more agony. But His reminder to me was that His grace and strength were sufficient – as they had been for those I had once put to death.

This time I was not taken to the headquarters of the Praetorian prefect; I was arriving as a prisoner who had already been condemned to death. I was not coming as one who had appealed to Caesar. In some respects, I was coming as a prize to be presented to Caesar. This time I would not be enjoying the comfort of private lodgings. Instead, I was taken to the Tullianum, where I would remain until the day of my execution.

Luke and Aristarchus arrived one month later. Their journey had primarily been over land. They had crossed the Aegean Sea by ferry, and then traveled for three weeks on the Roman highway, the Egnatian Way, through Macedonia to Dyrrachium on the Adriatic Sea. After arranging passage on a ferry across that sea, they arrived in Italy. It was then another three-week journey by foot along the Appian Way before they arrived in Rome.

Prior to the arrival of Luke and Aristarchus, the believers in Rome did not know I was there. I was not allowed to send any messages, and word had not yet reached them I was to be executed. My prison was cold and dank, and I had no blanket or cloak. I had not been permitted to bring anything with me the day I was taken from Troas. Food was rare; my jailers would provide me with something to eat occasionally. It was just enough to keep me alive. Prisoners relied on the kindness of friends outside the prison to provide them with food and blankets. Since no one knew I was there, I went without that first month.

Thankfully, that changed when Luke and Aristarchus arrived. My friends in Rome quickly learned of my captivity and began to provide me with what they could. As a Christian, I was considered an enemy of Rome, so the guards were not motivated to treat me well. For food or clothing to be passed to me, they expected to be given bribes. I was greatly surprised when they permitted Luke and Aristarchus to join me in my cell. But then I realized it meant they would receive even more bribes to provide for the needs of those men.

I received messages from Aquila and Claudia, as well as Pudens and Priscilla. They were making pleas on my behalf with fellow members of the senate who would be sympathetic to my plight. But their influence as senators had greatly diminished in recent days due to their standing as Christians under Nero's rule. Though their efforts were unsuccessful, I was grateful for all they continued to do at great personal risk to meet my physical needs. Julius, because of his position within the Praetorian guard, was able to visit me on occasion. He became an important lifeline to everyone outside of the prison.

Six months after my arrival in Rome, I was brought before a judge. I was surprised not one of my brothers or sisters was in the hall of judgment when I entered. I expected them to be there to bear witness on my behalf. It wasn't until several weeks later I learned they had attempted to be there but had been denied access. Since they were known Christians, their testimony was considered irrelevant.

The judge read the letter from the governor of Troas. He then asked me if I had anything to say before he ruled on my execution. I told him the accusations of revolt and rebellion against me were false. Quite to the contrary, I have taught:

"Everyone must submit to governing authorities. For all authority comes from God, and those in positions of authority have been placed there by God. So anyone who rebels against authority is rebelling against what God has instituted, and they will be punished. Pay your taxes, too, for these same reasons. For government workers need to be paid. They are serving God in what they do. Pay your taxes and government fees to those who collect them, and give respect and honor to those who are in authority."(2)

The judge reminded me there was no one there to speak on my behalf, but many had given testimony to the contrary in Troas. I had already been tried and convicted in Troas. His role was not to revisit the verdict; rather, his role was to determine the form of punishment. "Besides," he said, "you have already admitted to being a Christian, and Emperor Nero has declared all Christians are insurrectionists! Therefore, you are condemned to death by crucifixion or in the form of *"damnatio ad bestias"* (condemnation to beasts). You will either be nailed to a cross or placed in a pit to be eaten by a wild lion while our citizens watch and are entertained!"

"Your honor," I replied, "I know that you are knowledgeable of Roman law. Is it permissible under the law for you to sentence a Roman citizen to crucifixion or damnatio ad bestias?"

"Are you a Roman citizen?" the judge asked.

"I am a citizen by birth. I was born in the city of Tarsus and am the son of Jacob, who was also a Roman citizen!" I declared.

For the first time since I had entered the hall, the judge looked unsure of himself.

"Why has no one told me this man is a Roman citizen?" he asked of no one in particular. He then abruptly directed the guards to take me back to my cell while he investigated my claim of citizenship.

I was not afraid to die. I was willing to follow my Lord wherever and however He would lead. But I did not believe my Lord would have them make my death a spectacle of entertainment. My prayer was God would be glorified through my life and my death. So, as I returned to my cell, I did so knowing my Lord had intervened on my behalf before the judge. I would continue to entrust the outcome to Him.

. . .

A few weeks later, Tychicus and Demas arrived from Colossae and Titus and Crescens from Nicopolis. I was grateful for the effort these brothers had made and for the news they brought about the churches. They assured me of the prayers of intercession being lifted up on my behalf by all the believers. Their visit gave me opportunity to write letters of encouragement to the churches.

I was so happy to see the strength and confidence in the Lord of these men during such widespread persecution. But I was disappointed to discover two days later that Demas had swiftly departed for Thessalonica. He had confided to Tychicus he was afraid they would all be put to death because of their association with me. He had allowed fear to reign in his heart and displace his confidence in our Lord.

After a few weeks together, I sent Crescens and Titus away with my letters to the churches of Asia and Macedonia, respectively. I also dispatched Tychicus with a letter to Timothy in Ephesus. In the letter, I wrote:

"Timothy, my dear son,
Please come as soon as you can. Bring Mark with you when you come, for he will be helpful to me in my ministry. I am sending Tychicus to you, so he can continue the work while you are gone. *When you come, be sure to bring the coat I left with Carpus at Troas. Also bring my books, and especially my papers.*
Do your best to get here before winter.
May the Lord be with your spirit. And may His grace be with all of you."[3]

The days began to pass quickly. It appeared I would not be here to receive Timothy and Mark when they arrived – I expect to be in the presence of my Savior by then. Last week, I was brought to the hall of judgment to appear before the judge a second time. Again, I was not permitted to have any witnesses speak on my behalf. In fact, the judge had forbidden me from seeing any of the Roman believers, including Julius.

As I stood there awaiting the arrival of the judge, I turned my gaze heavenward. I was looking into the faces of a great cloud of witnesses. I could make out the faces of Stephen ... Parmenas ... Simon Peter ... and countless others. Each one was reminding me to keep my eyes on Jesus, on whom our faith depends from start to finish. Then the cloud of witnesses parted, and I saw there in their midst seated on His throne high and lifted up in all of His radiance – my Lord Jesus Christ.

When the judge entered, he declared, "Paul of Tarsus, I have been able to confirm you are in fact a Roman citizen. As you pointed out when you last stood before me, your citizenship prevents me from sentencing you to death in the form of crucifixion or damnatio ad bestias. But there is sufficient evidence you deserve the punishment due any citizen who has committed treason. Emperor Nero himself is aware of our proceedings today. He has directed me to tell you, 'As one of the leaders of the group of insurgents called Christians, you have turned this city and parts of this empire upside down. Your citizenship does not afford you any mercy. We will purge all the Christians from this land whether they be Jew, Gentile, or Roman.'

"Therefore, under the laws of Rome and the edict of the emperor, I command you be put to death by beheading. Guards, return him to his cell to await his execution." I was not permitted to speak. Judgment had been passed.

As I returned to my cell, I was acutely aware that my brothers and sisters were no longer with me, except for Luke and Aristarchus. God had permitted them to be here with me to the very end. Though my life on this earth is approaching its end, the work is not. The Spirit of God began this work, and He who has begun it will continue His work until it is finally finished on the day when Christ Jesus returns.

I have encouraged Luke to prepare a written account of the Gospel of Jesus, so it is available to the Gentile believers. Luke, in his giftedness as a physician, will provide a narrative that has been carefully investigated to provide the facts surrounding the life, death, and resurrection of Jesus. I have also encouraged him to record an account of the acts of the apostles so there is a clear record of how the Spirit of the Lord breathed life into the formation of His church, the body of Christ. These written accounts will serve to help the believers pass this knowledge and understanding from one generation to the next until the day of our Lord's return.

Aristarchus has helped me record this written account of the inexhaustible grace and unmerited favor my Lord has extended to me – a sinner. God has enabled him to endure many trials and hardships with me for the sake of the Gospel. He has never fainted nor grown weary in doing what is right. Many times, he has been the one by my side to encourage me and help me take the next step. I have asked him to return to Thessalonica, when the end comes, to continue the work that has begun there.

As for me, my life has already been poured out as an offering to God. The time of my death has dawned. I have fought the good fight, I have finished the race, and I have remained faithful. And now the prize awaits me – the crown of righteousness, which the Lord, the righteous Judge, will give me on the day of His return. And the prize is not just for me but for all who eagerly look forward to His appearing.[(4)]

As for you who have read this written account, *fight the good fight for the true faith. Hold tightly to the eternal life to which God has called you, which you have declared so well before many witnesses. And I charge you before God, who gives life to all, and before Christ Jesus, who gave a good testimony before Pontius Pilate, that you obey this command without wavering. Then no one can find fault with you from now until our Lord Jesus Christ comes again.*[(5)]

The guards have just arrived at my cell to take me to my executioner. `Here is my final greeting in my own hand – Paul. Remember my chains. May the grace of God be with you.`[(6)]

* * *

EPILOGUE

Now may the God of peace make you holy in every way, and may your whole spirit and soul and body be kept blameless until our Lord Jesus Christ comes again. God will make this happen, for He who calls you is faithful.[(1)]

* * *

In ancient times the Phoenicians, Carthaginians, and Romans – aided by their beliefs in Greek mythology – believed that Hercules had set two pillars, one on each side of the Strait of Gibraltar. The narrow strait connects the Atlantic Ocean with the Mediterranean Sea and separates southern Europe from northern Africa. We now know those pillars to be the Rock of Gibraltar to the north and the Jebel Musa in Morocco to the south. These two "pillars" flank the entrance to the Strait of Gibraltar.

The pillars were said to have been put in place by Hercules to designate the edge of the world. The ancients believed the world was flat and that sailing vessels would fall off the edge if they sailed beyond the horizon. Therefore, the pillars were deemed to mark a boundary beyond which no man should go. As such, a warning was inscribed on the rocks – "NON PLUS ULTRA" – meaning "nothing more beyond." These words carried the urgent warning to any who would attempt to pass – NOTHING MORE BEYOND.

The warning was believed to be truth and remained in place until Christopher Columbus discovered the New World at the end of the 15th century. Following that discovery, King Charles V of Spain had the negative word "NON" expunged to change the inscriptions from a warning of "nothing more beyond" into a reminder that there was "MORE BEYOND." The modified inscription further served as a reminder of the King's mission to extend the spread of Christianity throughout the newly discovered lands. Thus, it became even more than a reminder – it became a challenge.

In many ways, the message PLUS ULTRA is the message of the Gospel. We are to let the world know that there is MORE BEYOND. Our lives, our actions, and our words are to bear that inscription. We are to be bearers of that inscription and that message across the street in Jerusalem, down the road in Judea, outside of our comfort zone in Samaria, and to every corner extending to the very ends of the earth.

Because the reality is that for those who do not have a personal relationship with Christ, there is NO MORE BEYOND. Apart from a saving relationship with Christ, our sin has destined us all for an eternity separated from Him – not in eternal life, but in eternal death. Sin is in fact that negative word "NON." But through Christ's death, burial, and resurrection, He made the way for that negative word "NON" caused by our sin to be expunged – and in exchange He gave us more beyond – eternal and abundant life He has gone ahead to prepare for us. Life we can only have through Him if we will but receive it. Jesus's words to each of us are MORE BEYOND. They are words of LIFE – abundant life here, eternal life beyond. It is the life He gave us by laying down His own.

As we've been reminded throughout the pages of this novel – and see recorded throughout the Book of Acts and the epistles – the apostle Paul and others committed their lives to bear witness of the Gospel that there is

MORE BEYOND. They were willing to go where they had never been before to preach the Gospel to those who had never heard. They were willing to stay and stand firm for the sake of the Gospel, even when those around them turned against them. They were willing to do whatever was required to make Christ known.

i fear we often look at Paul, the other apostles, and other believers in the New Testament who spread the Gospel as being equipped in ways that seem beyond our grasp. We see them as extraordinary people for extraordinary times. We see them as so far above and beyond us that we could never do what they did. We have deceived ourselves into thinking we could never be that selfless, that fearless, or that full of faith.

My hope is that i have been able to convey the truth that these men and women were ordinary people empowered by an extraordinary God. In His sovereignty, He placed them in the time in which they lived for the work He was doing in that day. It wasn't their unique ability that set them apart; it was their unswerving availability to be used by the Holy Spirit who empowered them and went before them.

That same Holy Spirit indwells within each one of us if we have surrendered our lives to the Lord Jesus Christ. He has placed us in this day and time for His same continuing purpose. He has placed His Spirit within us to equip us and empower us for His mission. The mission task is not finished. We are a part of that continuing mission and it will not be completed until everyone on the face of the earth has heard the Gospel message that Jesus saves, He has paid the price for our sins, and there is MORE BEYOND in a personal relationship with Him.

We have no idea what twists and turns lie ahead of us, any more than Paul and his companions did. But just like He did for Paul, the Father has given us His Holy Spirit to guide, enable, equip, and comfort us as we follow Him in that path. And He has given us clear instruction as to what we are to be about: "*You will be My witnesses, telling people about Me everywhere—in Jerusalem, throughout Judea, in Samaria, and to the ends of the earth.*"[2]

. . .

Like Paul, each one of us has been called to be a part of God's mission and each one of us has been sent. God's plan for you may not be to travel halfway around the world ... but it might be! But for all of us, it will be to share the Good News with those He places in our path – our neighbors next door, those across the street, those across town, those across the country, or those in another part of the world. The point is, we are to go wherever He sends us. We don't need another invitation to go. Jesus has already given us His command. To do anything less is disobedience to Him.

Paul's story may already be written, and his race may already be finished, but ours isn't. Heed his challenge:

"Therefore I, a prisoner for serving the Lord, beg you to lead a life worthy of your calling, for you have been called by God."(3)

And may the grace of our Lord Jesus Christ be with you as you go!

* * *

PLEASE HELP ME BY LEAVING A REVIEW!

i would be very grateful if you would leave a review of this book. Your feedback will be helpful to me in my future writing endeavors and will also assist others as they consider picking up a copy of the book.

To leave a review:

Go to: amazon.com/dp/1734934581

Or scan this QR code using your camera on your smartphone:

Thanks for your help!

* * *

BE SURE TO CHECK OUT ...

... the other books in the *"Through The Eyes"* Series

Experience the truths of Scripture as these stories unfold through the lives and eyes of a shepherd, a spy and a prisoner. Rooted in biblical truth, these fictional novels will enable you to draw beside the storytellers as they worship the Baby in the manger, the Son who took up the cross, the Savior who conquered the grave, the Deliverer who parted the sea and the Eternal God who has always had a mission.

Book #1

Though the Eyes of a Shepherd

A Novel — **Shimon was a shepherd boy when he first saw the newborn King in a Bethlehem stable.** Join him in his journey as he re-encounters the Lamb of God at the Jordan, and follows the Miracle Worker through the wilderness, the Messiah to the cross, and the Risen Savior from the upper room. Though Shimon is a fictional character, we'll see the pages of the Gospels unfold through his eyes, and **experience a story of redemption – the redemption of a shepherd – and the redemption of each one who chooses to follow the Good Shepherd.**

Available through Amazon

Book #2

Though the Eyes of a Spy

A Novel — **Caleb was one of God's chosen people** – a people to whom He had given a promise. Caleb never forgot that promise — as a slave in Egypt, a spy in the Promised Land, a wanderer in the wilderness, or a conqueror in the hill country. We'll see the promise of Jehovah God unfold through his eyes, and **experience a story of God's faithfulness – to a spy who trusted Him – and to each one of us who will do the same.**

Available through Amazon.

* * *

Available in paperback, large print, and for Kindle on Amazon.

Scan this QR code using your camera on your smartphone to see the entire series.

"THE CALLED" SERIES

Stories of these ordinary men and women called by God to be used in extraordinary ways.

A Carpenter Called Joseph (Book 1)

A Prophet Called Isaiah (Book 2)

A Teacher Called Nicodemus (Book 3)

A Judge Called Deborah (Book 4)

A Merchant Called Lydia (Book 5)

A Friend Called Enoch (Book 6)

A Fisherman Called Simon (Book 7)

A Heroine Called Rahab (Book 8)

A Witness Called Mary (Book 9)

A Cupbearer Called Nehemiah (Book 10)

Available in paperback, large print, and for Kindle on Amazon.

Scan this QR code using your camera on your smartphone to see the entire series.

* * *

"THE PARABLES" SERIES

An Elusive Pursuit (Book 1)

(*releasing October 20, 2023*)

Twenty-three year old Eugene Fearsithe boarded a train on the first day of April 1912 in pursuit of his elusive dream. Little did he know where the journey would take him, or what . . . and who . . . he would discover along the way.

* * *

A Belated Discovery (Book 2)

(*releasing Spring 2024*)

Nineteen year old Bobby Fearsithe enlisted in the army on the fifteenth day of December 1941 to fight for his family, his friends, and his neighbors. Along the way, he discovered just who his neighbor truly was.

* * *

For more information, go to *kenwinter.org* or *wildernesslessons.com*

ALSO BY KENNETH A. WINTER

* * *

THE EYEWITNESSES

(a series of biblical fiction short story collections)

For Christmas/Advent

Little Did We Know – the advent of Jesus — for adults

Not Too Little To Know – the advent – ages 8 thru adult

For Easter/Lent

The One Who Stood Before Us – the ministry and passion of Jesus — for adults

The Little Ones Who Came – the ministry and passion – ages 8 thru adult

* * *

LESSONS LEARNED IN THE WILDERNESS SERIES

(a non-fiction series of biblical devotional studies)

The Journey Begins (Exodus) – Book 1

The Wandering Years (Numbers and Deuteronomy) – Book 2

Possessing The Promise (Joshua and Judges) – Book 3

Walking With The Master (The Gospels leading up to Palm Sunday) – Book 4

Taking Up The Cross (The Gospels – the passion through ascension) – Book 5

Until He Returns (The Book of Acts) – Book 6

ALSO AVAILABLE AS AUDIOBOOKS

THE CALLED

(the complete series)

A Carpenter Called Joseph

A Prophet Called Isaiah

A Teacher Called Nicodemus

A Judge Called Deborah

A Merchant Called Lydia

A Friend Called Enoch

A Fisherman Called Simon

A Heroine Called Rahab

A Witness Called Mary

A Cupbearer Called Nehemiah

* * *

Through the Eyes of a Shepherd

* * *

Little Did We Know

Not Too Little to Know

* * *

TIMELINE

The dates used in this timeline are approximations due to differences of opinion on the part of biblical scholars. They are not intended to provide historical accuracy, rather to provide a relative timeline for this novel. Also italicized names, events, or the timing of events listed in this timeline are either fictional or assumptions made for the purpose of telling the story.

* * *

Chapter 1 (*68 A.D.*)

Introduction

Chapter 2 (*5 – 25 A.D.*)

Paul's early years in Tarsus
Paul is a talmid under Rabbi Gamaliel in Jerusalem

Chapter 3 (*25 – 34 A.D.*)

Paul is back in Tarsus
Jesus is crucified in Jerusalem while Paul is in Tarsus (*29 A.D.*)

Chapter 4 (*34 – 35 A.D.*)

Paul returns to Jerusalem

Chapter 5 (*35 A.D.*)

Paul is on the road to Damascus

Chapter 6 (*35 A.D.*)

Paul is in Damascus with Ananias *and Nicanor*

Chapter 7 (*35 A.D.*)

Paul travels to Mount Hermon, Hippos and Gerasa

Chapter 8 (*35 – 36 A.D.*)

Paul is in Gerasa and the Decapolis city of Philadelphia

Chapter 9 (*36 – 37 A.D.*)

Paul is imprisoned in Petra

Chapter 10 (*38 A.D.*)

Paul is on Mount Sinai, in Pella, and returns to Damascus

Chapter 11 (*38 A.D.*)

Paul is in Jerusalem with Barnabas, Peter and James

Chapter 12 (*38 – 39 A.D.*)

Paul is shipwrecked off Cyprus and returns to Tarsus

Chapter 13 (*39 – 40 A.D.*)

Paul is in Cilicia – *in Aegeae and on the road to Anazarbus*

Chapter 14 (*40 – 43 A.D.*)

Paul is in Anazarbus, Hierapolis, Seleucia and Salamis

Chapter 15 (*43 – 45 A.D.*)

Paul is back in Tarsus

Chapter 16 (*46 – 47 A.D.*)

Paul and Barnabas are together in Antioch

Chapter 17 (*47 A.D.*)

Paul and Barnabas bring aid to the Church in Jerusalem

Chapter 18 (*47 A.D.*)

A devastating earthquake occurs
Paul and Barnabas are sent out on a mission journey by the Church in Antioch

Chapter 19 (*47 – 48 A.D.*)

Paul and Barnabas continue in their mission journey

Chapter 20 (*48 A.D.*)

Paul and Barnabas return to Antioch
A conflict arises within the Church between Jewish and Gentile believers

Chapter 21 (*49 A.D.*)

Paul and Barnabas appear before the council in Jerusalem
Paul and Barnabas disagree over John Mark

Chapter 22 (*49 – 50 A.D.*)

Paul and Silas are sent out by the Church in Antioch on the second mission journey

Chapter 23 (*50 – 51 A.D.*)

The second mission journey continues

Chapter 24 (*51 – 53 A.D.*)

The second mission journey concludes and the third begins

Chapter 25 (*53 – 57 A.D.*)

The third mission journey continues

Chapter 26 (*57 A.D.*)

Paul returns to Jerusalem and is arrested in the temple

Chapter 27 (*57 – 59 A.D.*)

Paul is imprisoned in Caesarea Maritima

Chapter 28 (*59 – 60 A.D.*)

Paul is taken to Rome to appeal before Caesar

Chapter 29 (*60 – 62 A.D.*)

Paul is under house arrest in Rome

Chapter 30 (*63 – 67 A.D.*)

Paul travels to Crete, Spain, Greece and Asia
Peter is martyred in Rome
Paul is arrested in Troas

Chapter 31 (*67 – 68 A.D.*)

Paul is imprisoned in Rome
Paul is executed

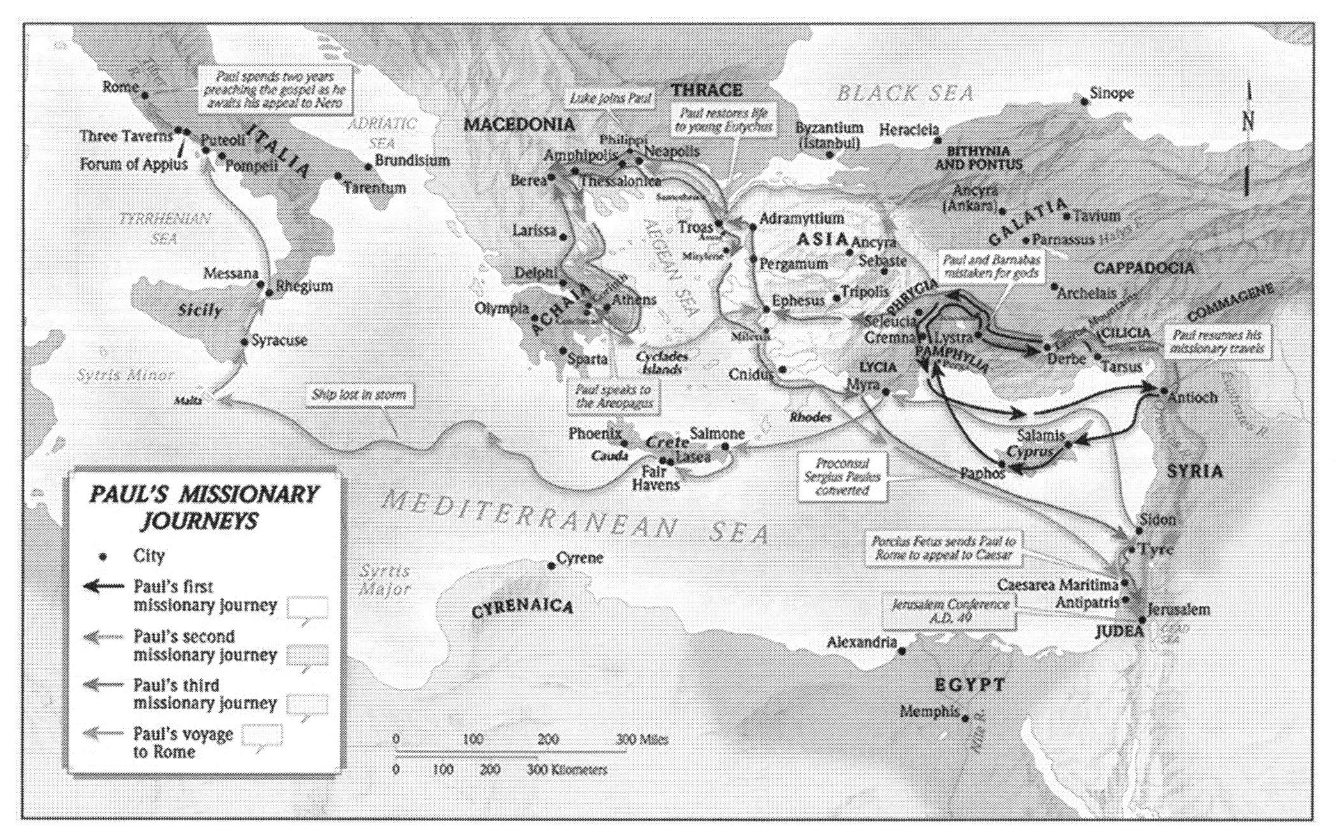

Paul's Missionary Journey Map by Broadman & Holman Publishers © 2003 – Reprinted and used by permission.

LISTING OF CHARACTERS

* * *

Many of the characters in this book are real people pulled directly from the pages of Scripture – most notably Jesus and Paul! i have not changed any details about a number of those individuals – again, most notably Jesus – except the addition of their interactions with the fictional characters. They are noted below as "UN" (unchanged).

In other instances, fictional details have been added to real people to provide backgrounds about their lives where Scripture is silent – again, most notably Paul. The intent is that you understand these were real people, whose lives were full of the many details that fill our own lives. They had a history before they were introduced in Scripture – and most of their stories continue well after their reference in the Bible. They are noted as "FB" (fictional background).

In some instances, we are never told the names of certain individuals in the Bible. In those instances, where i have given them a name as well as added fictional details, they are noted as "FN" (fictional name).

Lastly, several of the characters are purely fictional, added to convey the fictional elements of these stories. They are noted as "FC" (fictional character).

The characters are listed in order by the chapter in which they are first introduced in the novel. i have also added the chapter numbers in which they appear or are referenced.

* * *

(In order of first appearance, by chapter)

Jesus - *Son of God* (UN 1-31)

Paul/ Saul - *talmid of Gamliel - persecutor of the church - apostle to the Gentiles* (FB 1-31)

Aristarchus - *early believer in Thessalonica with noble background - companion of Paul* (FB 1,22,23,25,27-31)

Jason - *early believer in Thessalonica* (UN 1,23)

Silas/ Silvanus - *servant leader and teacher in Jerusalem church - sent to Antioch by James - companion of Paul* (FB 1,21-26)

Unnamed politarch in Thessalonica - *father of Aristarchus* (FB 1,23)

Abiel - *father of Jacob - grandfather of Paul – tentmaker - Pharisee - lived in Tarsus* (FC 2)

Aphiah - *father of Becorath - ancestor of Paul - fought with Judas Maccabaeus* (FC 2)

Becorath - *father of Zeror - ancestor of Paul - Pharisee in Jerusalem* (FC 2)

Dinah - *sister of Paul* (FN 2,3,12,15,22,24)

Emperor Augustus - *Caesar over Roman Empire 27 BC – 14 AD* (UN 2,30)

Gera - *father of Sheba - ancestor of Paul - Pharisee in Jerusalem* (FC 2)

Herod Archelaus - *fifth son of Herod the Great - ruled over Judea 2 BC - 6 AD* (UN 2,16)

Herod the Great - *tetrarch over all the provinces of Israel and Syria 37 – 2BC* (UN 2,7,9,16)

Jacob - *father of Paul from Tarsus – tentmaker - Pharisee* (FN 2,3)

John - *son of Zebedee - brother of James - apostle of Jesus* (FB 2,4,17,24)

Joseph – *eleventh son of Israel - prime minister of Egypt* (UN 2)

Judas Maccabaeus - *led Jews to independence from Seleucid Empire* (UN 2)

Leah - *daughter of Annas - wife of Caiaphas* (FN 2)

Mnason - *friend of Paul - became believer and elder of Jerusalem church* (FB 2,4,5,11,17,21,24,26)

Rabbi Caiaphas - *high priest 18 - 36 AD* (FB 2,4,8,11)

Rabbi Gamaliel - *grandson of Hillel - teacher of Paul* (FB 2,4,10,11,14,17)

Rabbi Hillel - *the elder - respected teacher of Israel* (FB 2,17)

Sheba - *father of Abiel - great-grandfather of Paul - tentmaker - Pharisee - moved to Tarsus from Jerusalem* (FC 2)

Unnamed mother of Paul from Tarsus (FB 2,3)

Valerius Gratus - *fourth prefect of Iudaea 15 – 26 AD* (UN 2)

Zeror - *father of Gera - ancestor of Paul - Pharisee in Jerusalem* (FC 2)

Arsakes - *childhood friend of Paul - magistrate – Tarsus* (FC 3,12,15,22,26)

Ashmus - *childhood friend of Paul - philosopher – Tarsus* (FC 3,12,15,21,23)

Benjamin - *childhood friend of Paul - rabbi – Tarsus* (FC 3,12,15)

Hezron - *son of Reuben & Dinah - nephew of Paul - traveled with Paul on third missionary journey* (FN 3,12,15,22,24-26)

Reuben - *husband of Dinah - brother-in-law of Paul* (FC 3,12,15,22,24,26)

Junius - *son of Theodatus Vettenus - persecutor with Saul* (FC 4,5)

Pontius Pilate - *fifth prefect of Iudaea 26 – 36 AD - father of Aquila II* (FB 4,29)

Rabbi Annas - *high priest 6 - 15 AD* (FB 4)

Rabbi Theodatus Vettenus - *chief priest of Cyrenian synagogue in Jerusalem* (FN 4)

Simon Peter - *apostle of Jesus* (FB 4,8,11,17,20,21,24,29-31)

Stephen/ Stephanos - *leader in Jerusalem church - stoned to death while Paul watched* (FB 4,11,17,19,22,31)

Ananias - *believer in Damascus - sent to Paul by God* (FB 5,6,10)

Judas - *tent merchant in Damascus - friend of Paul* (FC 5,6)

Nicanor - *leader in Jerusalem church - went to Damascus* (FB 5,6,10)

Nicolas of Antioch - *leader in Jerusalem church - renounced faith* (FB 5)

Parmenas - *leader in Jerusalem church – stoned to death* (FB 5,17,31)

Philip - *leader in Jerusalem church - the evangelist* (FB 5,10,26)

Procorus - *became believer on Day of Pentecost - leader in Jerusalem church - went to Seleucia, then to Tyre* (FB 5,14,15,26)

Timon - *leader in Jerusalem church - went to Cilicia* (FB 5,13,14,16)

Enos - *demoniac delivered by Jesus - living in Hippos* (FN 7,8,9,11)

Malchus - *servant of Caiaphas - Peter cut off his ear - living in Philadelphia* (FN 8-11)

Rachel - *daughter of high priest Caiaphas and Leah - became believer* (FC 8)

Aretas - *king of the Nabateans – father of Phasaelis* (FB 9,10,17)

Emperor Caligula - *Caesar over Roman Empire 37 - 41 AD* (UN 9)

Emperor Tiberius - *Caesar over Roman Empire 14 - 37 AD* (UN 9,17,18)

Herod Antipas - *sixth son of Herod the Great - ethnarch over Galilee and Perea 2 BC - 39 AD* (FB 9,16,17,27)

Herodias - *divorced her first husband Herod II to marry Herod Antipas* (UN 9,16)

John the baptizer – *sent by God to prepare the way for Jesus* (FB 9,16)

Lucius Vitellius the Elder - *governor of Syria 35 – 39 AD* (UN 9)

Obodas - *blind man who receives sight in Petra* (FC 9)

Phasaelis - *daughter of King Aretas - divorced first wife of Herod Antipas* (UN 9)

Yanzu - *servant to one of the magi (Balthazar) who brought a gift to Jesus in Bethlehem - Parthian scholar living in Petra* (FC 9)

Alexander Jannaeus - *Hasmonean king 103 – 76 BC* (UN 10)

Barnabas/ Joseph - *cousin of Mnason - co-laborer with Paul* (FB 11,15-21,25,26,29)

James – *half brother of Jesus - pastor and elder of church in Jerusalem* (FB 11,16,17,21,24,16)

Jude – *half brother of Jesus* (FB 11)

Esther - *daughter of Reuben & Dinah - niece of Paul* (FC 12,15,22)

Luke - *the physician – companion of Paul* (FB 12,13,16-18,20,22,23,25-31)

Marius - *Roman soldier in Aegeae - became believer* (FC 13,16)

Unnamed Roman commander in Aegeae (FC 13)

Arsames - *tent merchant in Anazarbus - friend of Paul* (FC 14)

Isabella - *wife of Arsames* (FC14)

Servilius - *brother of Arsames - living in Hierapolis* (FC 14)

Thoros - *son of Arsames – traveled with Paul* (FC 14)

Andri - *captain of Cypriot trading ship* (FC 15,18)

Rachel - *daughter of Reuben & Dinah - niece of Paul* (FC 15,22)

Tomys - *brother of Andri - tentmaker - lives in Salamis* (FC 15,18)

Unnamed father of Andri - *tentmaker - lives in Salamis* (FC 15)

Chuza - *household manager of Herod Antipas - follower of Jesus* (FB 16)

Joanna - *wife of Chuza - follower of Jesus* (FB 16)

Lucius - *Jew from Cyrene - cousin of Simon who carried Jesus's cross - elder of church at Antioch* (FB 16,18,20)

Manaen - Essene who grew up in Herod's palace - elder of church at Antioch (FB 16-18,20)

Samuel - *son of Chuza & Joanna - healed by Jesus* (FN 16)

Simeon - *Gentile from Nubia - elder of church at Antioch* (FB 16-18,20)

Simon the Cyrene - *pulled from the crowd to carry the cross of Jesus* (FB 16,30)

Unnamed father of Luke (FB 16,18)

Unnamed father of Manaen - *counselor to Herod the Great* (FB 16)

Unnamed mother of Luke (FB 16,18)

Agabus - *a prophet from Jerusalem* (UN 17,26)

Emperor Claudius - *Caesar over Roman Empire 41 - 54 AD* (UN 17,24)

James - *son of Zebedee, brother of John, apostle of Jesus* (FB 17)

John Mark - *son of Mary - cousin of Barnabas - companion of Paul* (FB 17,18,20,21,26,29,31)

King Agrippa I - *governor of Judea, Samaria, Galilee and Perea* (UN 17,27)

Mary - *mother of John Mark - aunt of Barnabas and Mnason* (FB 17)

Rhoda - *servant of Mary, the mother of John Mark* (UN 17)

Theophilus - *friend of Luke - governor of Antioch* (FB 17,18)

Valerian - *father of Theophilus - governor of Antioch, prior to Theophilus* (FC 17)

Zebedee - *father of James and John* (UN 17)

Andreas - *captain of Cypriot trading ship - from Salamis* (FC 18,20)

Aurelius - *believer in Antioch killed in earthquake* (FC 18)

Elymas - *Jewish sorcerer in Paphos* (FB 18)

Hasan - *believer in Salamis* (FC 18)

Rufus - *Christian in Antioch killed in earthquake* (FC 18)

Sergio Paulus - *proconsul of Cyprus* (FB 18)

Unnamed daughter of Theophilus (FC 18)

Unnamed son of Theophilus (FC 18)

Eunice - *mother of Timothy* (FB 19,22)

Lois - *grandmother of Timothy* (FB 19,22)

Neoptolemus - *Gentile father of Timothy* (FN 19,22,24)

Quintus - *city official in Antioch in Pisidia - a believer* (FC 19)

Timothy - *companion of Paul from Lystra* (FB 19,20,22-26,29,31)

Joazar - *Jewish believer in Jerusalem - former Pharisee* (FC 21)

Joseph Barsabbas - *one of seventy sent out by Jesus - brother of Judas Barsabbas* (FB 21)

Judas Barsabbas - *one of seventy sent out by Jesus - brother of Joseph Barsabbas* (FB 21)

Matthias - *one of seventy sent out by Jesus - chosen to be twelfth apostle* (UN 21,24)

Sabbas - *father of Judas Barsabbas and Joseph Barsabbas* (UN 21)

Benjamin - *son of Reuben & Dinah - nephew of Paul* (FC 22)

Alexander the Great - *ruled Macedonia after his father King Philip II* (UN 23)

Damaris - *wife of Dionysius - early believer in Athens* (FB 23)

Dionysius - *judge in Athens - early believer* (FB 23)

King Philip II - *king of Macedonia* (UN 23)

Lydia - *freeborn single woman from Thyatira - seller of purple cloth - first believer in Philippi* (FB 23)

Secundus - *a slave in Thessalonica who became an early believer - companion of Paul* (UN 23,25)

Unnamed duumviri in Philippi (UN 23)

Unnamed father of Dionysius (FC 23)

Unnamed jailer in Philippi (FB 23)

Unnamed slave girl - *possessed by a demon in Philippi* (UN 23)

Abram - *participated in stoning of Paul in Lystra - later became a believer* (FC 24)

Andrew - *brother of Simon Peter, apostle of Jesus* (FB 24)

Aquila - *Jew expelled from Rome - tentmaker in Corinth - leader of Corinthian church - companion of Paul* (FB 24,25)

Bartholomew/ Nathanael - *apostle of Jesus* (UN 24)

Crispus - *leader of synagogue in Corinth - early believer* (UN 24)

Emperor Nero - *Caesar over Roman Empire 54 - 68 AD* (FB 24,29-31)

Governor Gallio - *governor of Corinth* (UN 24)

Governor Quadratus - *governor of Syria* (UN 24,27)

James (the Less) - *son of Clopas - apostle of Jesus* (FB 24)

Matthew - *apostle of Jesus* (FB 24)

Philip - *apostle of Jesus* (UN 24)

Priscilla - *wife of Aquila - leader of church in Corinth - companion of Paul* (FB 24,25)

Rabbi Ananias - *son of Nedebeus - high priest 46-52 AD and 54-58 AD* (FB 24,27)

Simon the zealot - *apostle of Jesus* (FB 24)

Sosthenes - *leader of synagogue in Corinth, after Crispus - became believer - companion of Paul* (FB 24,25)

Thaddeus - *son of Clopas - apostle of Jesus* (FB 24)

Thomas - *apostle of Jesus* (FB 24)

Titius Justus - *early believer in Corinth* (UN 24)

Alexander - *metal worker and leader of synagogue in Ephesus - arranges Paul's arrest in Troas* (FB 25,30)

Apollos - *evangelist from Alexandria* (FB 25)

Demetrius - *silver worker in Ephesus* (UN 25)

Erastus - *city treasurer in Corinth - early believer - comes to Paul in Ephesus* (FB 25)

Gaius - *believer from Macedonia - companion with Aristarchus and Paul* (UN 25)

Sceva - *Jewish priest with seven sons in Ephesus* (UN 25)

Sopater - *believer from Berea - traveled with Paul* (FB 25)

Titus - *a Greek from Antioch of Syria - companion of Paul - entrusted with letter of correction to Corinthian church* (FB 25,30,31)

Trophimus - *Gentile believer from Ephesus - companion of Paul* (FB 25,26)

Tychicus - *believer from Ephesus - traveled with Paul* (UN 25,26,29,31)

Tyrannus - *headmaster of school in Ephesus* (FC 25)

Unnamed mayor of Ephesus (UN 25)

Claudius - *commander of Antonio Fortress in Jerusalem* (FB 26,27)

Eutychus - *young man who fell out of window in Troas* (FB 26)

Governor Marcus Antonius Felix - *governor of Judea 52 – 60 AD* (FB 26,27)

Azizus – *divorced first husband of Drusilla* (UN 27)

Bernice - *sister of King Agrippa II and his incestuous lover* (UN 27)

Drusilla - *wife of Marcus Antonius Felix and daughter of King Agrippa I* (UN 27)

Governor Porcius Festus - *governor of Judea 60 – 63 AD* (FB 27-29)

King Agrippa II - *great grandson of Herod the Great - governor of Galilee and Perea* (UN 27)

Rabbi Jonathan - *high priest 52 - 54 AD* (FB 27)

Tertullus - *lawyer representing high council in Paul's trial before Felix* (FN 27)

Julius - *captain of the imperial regiment responsible for delivering Paul to Rome* (FB 28,29,31)

Publius - *chief official of Malta* (FB 28)

Unnamed Egyptian ship's captain (FB 28)

Claudia - *wife of Pontius Pilate - mother of Aquila II - believer in Rome* (FB 29,31)

Demas - *believer from Macedonia - traveled to Rome with Tychicus - abandoned Paul* (FB 29,31)

Epaphroditus - *believer from Philippi - traveled to Rome with Timothy* (FB 29,30)

Eubulus - *Gentile believer in Rome* (FB 29,30)

Justus - *Jewish believer in Rome* (FB 29,30)

Linus - *Jewish believer in Rome* (FB 29)

Onesimus - *indentured bondservant to Philemon in Colossae - believer - traveled to Rome with Tychicus* (FB 29)

Philemon - *an elder of the church in Colossae* (UN 29)

Pontius Aquila I - *leader of opposition that overthrew Julius Caesar - great-grandfather of Aquila II* (FB 29)

Pontius Aquila II - *son of Pontius Pilate & Claudia - commanding officer of Praetorian guard - follower of Jesus* (FC 29,31)

Pontius Cominus – *father of Pontius Pilate - grandfather of Aquila II* (FC 29)

Priscilla - *wife of Pudens - believer in Rome* (FB 29,31)

Pudens - *member of Roman senate - believer in Rome* (FB 29,31)

Sextus Afranius Burrus - *prefect over the Praetorian guard in Rome* (FB 29)

Alexander - *son of Simon the Cyrene* (UN 30)

Antony - *Roman general - one of three joint leaders who ruled the Roman Republic 43 – 30 BC* (UN 30)

Aristocles - *teacher and philosopher in Messina, Sicily - became believer* (FC 30)

Cleopatra - *Queen of Egypt 51 – 30 BC - love interest of Antony* (UN 30)

Euodia - *a believer in Philippi whose disagreement with Syntyche had created division in the church* (UN 30)

Lucius - *young philosopher and teacher in Nicopolis - first believer in that city* (FC 30)

Polycarp - *a disciple of the apostle John and a leader of the 2nd century church - martyred at the stake* (FB 30)

Rufus - *son of Simon the Cyrene* (FB 30)

Syntyche - *a believer in Philippi whose disagreement with Euodia had created division in the church* (UN 30)

Unnamed governor in Troas - *condemns Paul to death* (FC 30)

Unnamed wife of Simon the Cyrene (FB 30)

Vetus - *wife of Lucius - one of first believers in Nicopolis* (FC 30)

Crescens - *believer from Nicopolis - travels to Rome with Titus* (FB 31)

Unnamed judge in Rome - *determined form of Paul's execution* (FC 31)

* * *

SCRIPTURE BIBLIOGRAPHY

Much of the story line of this book is taken from The Acts of the Apostles, as well as the Epistles written by the apostle Paul, as recorded in the New Testament of the Holy Bible. Certain fictional events or depictions of those events have been added.

Specific references and quotations:

Preface

(1) Ephesians 4:1
(2) Galatians 1:15-18
(3) Galatians 1:12
(4) Acts 9:20
(5) Galatians 1:21
(6) Acts 15:41
(7) Acts 11:25
(8) 2 Timothy 4:7
(9) Colossians 4:10
(10) Philemon 24

Chapter 1

(1) Acts 17:2
(2) Acts 17:3
(3) Acts 17:6-7

Chapter 2

[1] Acts 22:3
[2] Deuteronomy 6:6
[3] Deuteronomy 6:4-5

Chapter 3

[1] Acts 21:39
[2] Proverbs 27:17

Chapter 4

[1] Acts 7:58
[2] Acts 3:4
[3] Acts 3:6
[4] Acts 3:16, 19
[5] Acts 5:38-39
[6] John 1:1-4, 14
[7] Revelation 22:13
[8] Acts 6:11
[9] Acts 7:1
[10] Acts 7:47-53
[11] Acts 7:56
[12] Acts 7:60
[13] Acts 5:39

Chapter 5

[1] 1 Corinthians 15:9
[2] Acts 5:39
[3] Acts 9:4 (NASB)
[4] Acts 9:5 (NASB)
[5] Acts 9:5-6 (NASB)
[6] Acts 5:39
[7] Acts 9:6 (NASB)
[8] Acts 9:17
[9] Acts 9:15-16

Chapter 6

[1] Galatians 1:17
[2] Isaiah 53:3-6
[3] Acts 23:1

[4] Acts 26:4-5

[5] Acts 26:9-11

[6] Acts 26:12-16, 18-19

Chapter 7

[1] Galatians 1:12

[2] Psalm 133:3

[3] Isaiah 6:5 (ESV)

[4] Revelation 1:17-18

[5] Acts 9:15-16 (NASB)

[6] Mark 9:7

[7] Psalm 118:22

[8] Luke 7:30

[9] Acts 13:46-47, quoting Isaiah 49:6

[10] Acts 22:3-15

Chapter 8

[1] 2 Timothy 2:2

[2] Matthew 26:52-53

[3] Acts 18:6

Chapter 9

[1] 2 Corinthians 11:32

Chapter 10

[1] 2 Corinthians 11:33

[2] Isaiah 49:6

Chapter 11

[1] Acts 9:26

[2] Ephesians 3:8

[3] Mark 5:19 (ESV)

[4] Acts 22:17-21

Chapter 12

[1] Acts 9:30

[2] Acts 17:23-28

[3] Acts 17:30-31

Chapter 13

[1] Galatians 1:21
[2] Acts 13:38-41, quoting Habakkuk 1:5
[3] Matthew 6:14-15
[4] 2 Corinthians 3:7, 9-10
[5] 2 Corinthians 3:12, 17-18
[6] Matthew 5:15 (paraphrase)
[7] Genesis 22:18

Chapter 14

[1] 2 Corinthians 11:26
[2] Matthew 5:14
[3] Acts 13:38-39
[4] Ephesians 3:8
[5] Acts 27:18

Chapter 15

[1] 2 Corinthians 11:24-27
[2] Acts 22:6-7
[3] Acts 22:8-9
[4] Acts 22:10
[5] Acts 22:10
[6] Acts 22:14-15
[7] 1 Corinthians 2:1-2, 4-5
[8] 1 Corinthians 2:6-7
[9] Ephesians 1:9-11
[10] 2 Timothy 2:15-26 (paraphrase)

Chapter 16

[1] Acts 11:25-26
[2] Mark 10:47
[3] Mark 10:51
[4] Mark 10:51
[5] Mark 10:52
[6] John 19:30

Chapter 17

[1] Acts 11:29
[2] Acts 13:17-30

[3] 1 Corinthians 15:4-9
[4] Acts 12:14
[5] Acts 12:15

Chapter 18
[1] Acts 13:2
[2] Acts 13:2
[3] Acts 13:10-11
[4] Acts 13:15
[5] Acts 13:16
[6] Acts 13:38-39
[7] Acts 13:43 (NASB)

Chapter 19
[1] Acts 13:50-51
[2] Acts 14:10
[3] Acts 14:11
[4] Acts 14:15-17
[5] 2 Timothy 3:12, 14
[6] 1 Thessalonians 2:1, 4
[7] 2 Timothy 4:2

Chapter 20
[1] Acts 14:26
[2] Galatians 2:14
[3] Galatians 1:3-5
[4] Galatians 2:20 (ESV)
[5] Galatians 5:1
[6] Galatians 5:16
[7] Galatians 5:22-23
[8] Galatians 6:11-18
[9] Acts 15:1

Chapter 21
[1] Acts 15:5
[2] Genesis 17:4
[3] Genesis 17:9, 10
[4] Philippians 1:27
[5] Acts 15:7-11

[6] Acts 15:13-21 (quoting Amos 9:11-12)
[7] Matthew 19:28
[8] Acts 15:23-29

Chapter 22

[1] Acts 15:41
[2] 2 Corinthians 5:17-18 (ESV)
[3] 1 Corinthians 9:19-23
[4] 2 Timothy 2:2
[5] Acts 16:9

Chapter 23

[1] Acts 16:13
[2] Deuteronomy 4:29 (NIV)
[3] Acts 16:15
[4] Acts 16:17
[5] Acts 16:18
[6] Acts 16:20-21
[7] Acts 16:28
[8] Acts 16:30
[9] Acts 16:35
[10] Acts 16:36
[11] Acts 16:37
[12] Acts 17:6
[13] 1 Thessalonians 1:6-10
[14] Acts 17:18
[15] Acts 17:22-24, 27, 30-31
[16] Acts 17:32

Chapter 24

[1] Acts 18:1
[2] Acts 18:10
[3] Acts 18:13
[4] Acts 18:14-15

Chapter 25

[1] Acts 19:1
[2] Acts 19:13
[3] Acts 19:15

Chapter 26

[1] Acts 20:6
[2] Acts 20:10
[3] Acts 20:18-35
[4] 2 Timothy 2:10
[5] Philippians 1:20
[6] Acts 21:11
[7] Acts 21:25
[8] Acts 21:20-24
[9] Acts 21:28
[10] Acts 21:36
[11] Acts 21:37
[12] Acts 21:37-38
[13] Acts 21:39
[14] Acts 23:6
[15] Acts 23:11
[16] Acts 23:17
[17] Acts 23:22
[18] Acts 23:27-30

Chapter 27

[1] Acts 23:31-33
[2] Acts 23:35
[3] Acts 24:10-21
[4] Acts 26:2-3
[5] Acts 26:16-18
[6] Acts 26:19, 22-23
[7] Acts 26:25-27
[8] Acts 26:28 (NKJ)
[9] Acts 26:29
[10] Acts 26:31-32

Chapter 28

[1] Acts 27:1
[2] Acts 27:10
[3] Acts 27:21-26
[4] Acts 27:31
[5] Acts 27:33-34
[6] Acts 28:4

[7] Romans 1:18-19

Chapter 29

[1] Acts 28:16
[2] Acts 28:17-20
[3] Acts 28:21-22
[4] Acts 28:25-28
[5] 2 Timothy 2:4
[6] Ephesians 6:13-18
[7] Ephesians 3:17
[8] Philippians 4:8-9
[9] Colossians 3:12-13
[10] Philemon 8-12

Chapter 30

[1] 1 Timothy 1:3
[2] John 21:18

Chapter 31

[1] Colossians 4:18
[2] Romans 13:1-2, 6-7
[3] 2 Timothy 4:9, 11-13, 22
[4] 2 Timothy 4:6-8
[5] 1 Timothy 6:12-14
[6] Colossians 4:18

Epilogue

[1] 1 Thessalonians 5:23-24
[2] Acts 1:8
[3] Ephesians 4:1

ACKNOWLEDGMENTS

I do not cease to give thanks for you ....
Ephesians 1:16 (ESV)

... to my trusted companion and partner in the mission, LaVonne,
for choosing to trust God as we follow Him in this faith adventure together;

... to my family,
for your love, support and encouragement;

... to Sheryl,
for helping me tell the story of the mission of God much more effectively;

... to Dennis,
for the way you use your creative abilities to further the mission of God on a daily basis;

... to my team of advance readers,
for all of your help and encouragement;

... and most importantly,
to the One who is the Author and Finisher of the mission
– our Lord and Savior Jesus Christ!

ABOUT THE AUTHOR

Ken Winter is a follower of Jesus, an extremely blessed husband, and a proud father and grandfather – all by the grace of God. His journey with Jesus has led him to serve on the pastoral staffs of two local churches – one in West Palm Beach, Florida and the other in Richmond, Virginia – and as the vice president of mobilization of the IMB, an international missions organization.

Today, Ken continues in that journey as a full-time author, teacher and speaker. You can read his weekly blog posts at kenwinter.blog and listen to his weekly podcast at kenwinter.org/podcast.

* * *

And we proclaim Him, admonishing every man and teaching every man with all wisdom, that we may present every man complete in Christ. And for this purpose also I labor, striving according to His power, which mightily works within me.
(Colossians 1:28-29 NASB)

PLEASE JOIN MY READERS' GROUP

Please join my Readers' Group in order to receive updates and information about future releases, etc.

Also, i will send you a free copy of ***The Journey Begins*** e-book — the first book in the ***Lessons Learned In The Wilderness*** series. It is yours to keep or share with a friend or family member that you think might benefit from it.

It's completely free to sign up. i value your privacy and will not spam you. Also, you can unsubscribe at any time.

* * *

Go to kenwinter.org to subscribe. Or scan this QR code using your camera on your smartphone

Made in the USA
Columbia, SC
22 January 2024